*The Golden Flute*

# The Golden Flute

*AN ANTHOLOGY OF POETRY FOR YOUNG CHILDREN*

*Selected by*

ALICE HUBBARD

INSTRUCTOR AND DEMONSTRATION TEACHER IN THE JERSEY CITY STATE NORMAL SCHOOL, JERSEY CITY, NEW JERSEY

*and*

ADELINE BABBITT

DIRECTOR AND PRINCIPAL OF THE HENRY AND DOROTHY CASTLE MEMORIAL KINDERGARTEN AT HONOLULU, HAWAII

*with an introduction by*

PATTY SMITH HILL

PROFESSOR OF EDUCATION IN THE KINDERGARTEN DEPARTMENT AT TEACHERS COLLEGE, COLUMBIA UNIVERSITY

THE JOHN DAY COMPANY

*New York*

EIGHTHTEENTH PRINTING

PRINTED IN THE U. S. A.
FOR THE JOHN DAY COMPANY, INC.

# FOREWORD

This book was created to help those who are searching for that poetry which very young children enjoy.

In selecting the text we approached our problem from two angles: first, the interests of children from two to three years of age, of those from four to five years, and on up to nine years of age; and second, what children of these ages not only enjoy but understand in poetry.

To discover their interests it was necessary that we study not only records of children, but children themselves. We then searched for poems to fit these interests. Here we met with many obstacles, for the poetic interest of children is unusually varied, and available material scattered.

In order to find out what appealed to children we carefully studied the poems they like, and thus discovered the bases of attraction. We found that poems attracted for different reasons, such as:

- rhyme
- rhythm
- action or stimulation to imagination or thought
- dramatic appeal
- unusual words
- stories of animals or familiar experiences—life about them
- emotional appeal—if not too intense
- humor
- the guessing element—riddles

The poems we have selected have been gathered from poets old and new. And we have kept in mind the fact that children like simple, rather short poems, when they are very young, and increasingly longer poems as they grow older.

Children can best be helped to build an interest in poetry if a poem can be told when the child is having or has just had an experience, e.g.,—while walking in the country, a turtle might be seen, and if a poem such as "The Little Turtle" by Vachel Lindsay could be told or read, the interest in the turtle would increase. After many similar experiences a very real interest in poetry itself is gradually built up.

In order to have poems available quickly, so that they can be used when the interest is high (for the interest of young children very quickly shifts to another thought or activity) we have made beside the usual *Index to Author* and *Index to First Line* an *Index to Interest.* For the benefit of the reader we have placed each poem under as many headings as there are dominant thoughts in the content of the poem.

If poems can be used together with stories and songs to supplement interest, one can begin the cultivation of an appreciation for and pleasure in poetry and literature at an earlier age than was formerly thought possible.

THE EDITORS.

## INTRODUCTION

At last we have an anthology of verse for young children in which the editors have endeavored to develop the child's poetic aptitudes to their highest levels—avoiding on one hand valueless, nonsensical jingles which lead nowhere; and on the other, poems too mature in content and form for immature minds to grasp or appreciate. In other words, their problem has been to seek that poetry which voices the interests and interprets the experiences of very young children. They have sought for poetic forms of expression, not just to catch and hold attention, but to provide opportunities for continuity of growth in poetic appreciation from one age level to the next throughout the period of early childhood.

This volume, therefore, is the product of years of research in libraries and periodicals followed by experiments conducted by teachers and supervisors in Kindergartens and Primary grades in which the selections were put to the test of use. From their experience with children and teachers the editors were increasingly impressed with the dearth of good poetic material to stimulate and keep alive the little child's native poetic feeling which, without suitable developmental materials, often dies of inanition in early childhood.

Parents and teachers should anticipate the child's need for good poetry to interpret the experiences of work and play. The same intelligence and skill which teachers have displayed for many years in the use of songs and stories can likewise be expressed in this field.

No one has given a better statement of the function of art in life and education than Robert Browning in "Fra Lippo Lippi" when he says:

> "For, don't you mark? we're made so that we love
> First when we see them painted, things we have passed
> Perhaps a hundred times nor cared to see;

And so they are better, painted—better to us,
Which is the same thing. Art was given for that."

A practical exemplification of this took place in one of our kindergartens when the children were arranging the flowers and fruits to decorate the table for the Thanksgiving celebration. As they were putting on the last touches—the teacher began to sing very quietly and reverently, without accompaniment:

"All things bright and beautiful,
All things great and small,
All things wise and wonderful,
Our Father made them all."

One at a time the voices were hushed. The little hands and feet were still as the children looked up and crept nearer to the singer as she gave a new interpretation to the experiences through which they were passing through poetry and song.

This artistic and intelligent use of song and story is partly due to the adequate supply provided for such purposes. Unless the teachers of the future have an equally liberal supply of verse to serve in like manner, the child's love of poetry will be starved at a period of development when he most needs poetry. Poetry of excellence on the child's level of maturity will stimulate his natural tendencies to voice his own experiences and feelings in rhythmic form at a stage in his development when he tends to chant as naturally as he sings or speaks. In past years poetry was so neglected in early childhood that few parents or teachers of to-day recognize the poetic values in this early chanting, and the child's crude attempts to accompany activity with rhythmic language.

Dr. Hughes Mearns, through his experiments with children of all ages, opened the eyes of teachers to the unrecognized poetic abilities of children, which unseeing adults consciously or unconsciously repressed or failed to utilize. Those astonishing results made us wonder how many more Hilda Conklings there might have been in the world to-day had there been more sympathetic and understanding parents and teachers.

*The New Republic* in the issue of June 17, 1931, offers a number of beautiful poetic expressions from very young children which are well worth quoting as an illustration of this fact. Nannce, about four, chimes to some adult who understands and records for her:

### MUSIC

"Music makes me write—
It tells me to.
Some music is bended and patting,
And sorry for spanked children;
And some is awful,
Made with elbows and not fingers.
It tells dogs to bite,
And children to tear up books.
But the other ones are beautiful
As floating to the mountain
In the Ark of Noah.
A large one tells me to write this.
Its beginning is strong,
And makes the Noah's Ark float;
And its ending is love,
Near Mother."

### PHILOSOPHY

"Do you know that the light
Is brightest at the top of the stairs?
Dark is the place down.
Stairs are always going up.
Downstairs is the wrong way.
Light is large at the top."

### GENEROUS GARDEN

"That little tree
With a tiny low fence around it,
In a beautiful little garden.
She is a generous woman—
She made a garden,
And put a tiny pine tree
In its center.
I have little trees
But behind my eyes

I have flowers, too—
Rugs and rugs of them;
And earth is the floor,
As far, as far
As I make thinking go.
But she is a generous woman,
And put her little tree
Out in the garden
For me to see."

Terence, Thomas, and Philip, about the same age, also quoted, manifest poetic feeling, though not quite so lengthy, even when they voice their thought in a more limited form.

These appear remarkable to those unfamiliar with young children and yet to those who work and play intimately with little four year olds from day to day with an intelligent mind and an understanding heart are not sure that there may not be many little Nannces, Terences, Philips and Thomases, were there more parents and teachers who possessed sufficient poetic feeling themselves to enable them to recognize the beginnings of creative poetic development.

These creative expressions of young children may be no guarantee whatever of poetic ability in adult life, but they serve to prepare the way for the development of poetic appreciation. While it may be better for the public that many of us remain "mute, inglorious Miltons" in adult life, it is a tragedy to pass into mature years deaf to the beauty contributed to life through the poetic genius of the ages.

This collection of poems began when the compilers were graduate students in a university class making a study of children's literature. They selected the poetic aspects of children's literature for investigation, and not realizing at the outset the enormous amount of research this entailed, they were advised by their professors to carry on a more prolonged study which might develop their thesis into a collection worthy of publication. This anthology is the result, and as it stands it represents a wide knowledge of children's literature past and present. It is also the outcome of a long continued study of child interests growing out of years of experience in classroom teaching and supervision. The editors' background of experience and professional training has made it possible for them to not only select poetry measuring up to excellent literary standards, but poems meeting the developmental needs of immature minds. For the convenience of teachers the poems are classified and listed under the captions of "interests" and "subjects." Selected as they are from widely scattered sources and put into book form teachers can locate quickly any poem needed when interest is at its high-water mark. Untold time and strength is thus conserved. The poem which the "subject" requires must be within reach—at the teacher's finger tips, if it is to be read; or, better still, on the tip of her tongue to recite. Thus poetic feeling, so easily stirred in early life, is conserved, and increasing insight into the significance of life experience is deepened.

Patty Smith Hill.

Teachers College,
Columbia University,
New York City.

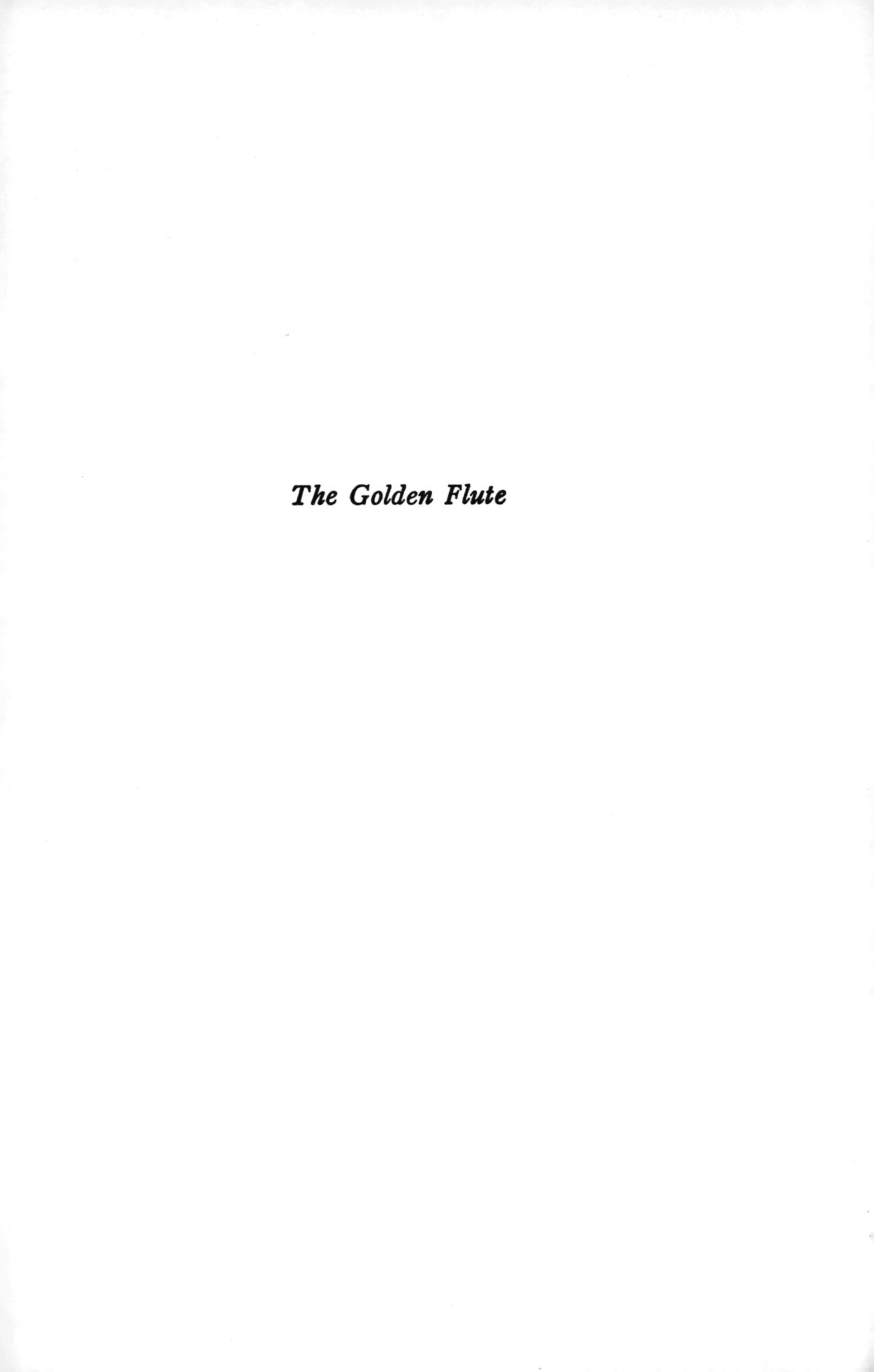

*The Golden Flute*

## ACORNS

Oh, when the ripe acorns,
So smooth and so brown,
Get loose from their cups
And come pattering down

What work is in store
For the girls and the boys,
First of all to collect them,
And then to make toys.

For they can make thimbles,
And tiny doll's cradles,
And thorn-handled saucepans,
And egg-cups and ladles,

Extinguishers, flower-pots,
Baskets and rings,
And barrels and buckets,
And all kinds of things.

They can stock a whole shop,
If they have any brains,
And use a small penknife,
And plenty of pains.

EDITH KING.

## AT THE SEA-SIDE

When I was down beside the sea
A wooden spade they gave to me
To dig the sandy shore.

My holes were empty like a cup.
In every hole the sea came up,
Till it could come no more.

ROBERT LOUIS STEVENSON.

## AT THE THEATER

The sun was bright when we went in,
But night and lights were there,
The walls had golden trimming on
And plush on every chair.

The people talked; the music played,
Then it grew black as pitch,
Yes, black as closets full of clothes,
Or caves, I don't know which.

The curtain rolled itself away,
It went I don't know where,
But, oh, that country just beyond,
I do wish we lived there!

The mountain peaks more jagged rise,
Grass grows more green than here;
The people there have redder cheeks,
And clothes more gay and queer.

They laugh and smile, but not the same,
Exactly as we do,
And if they ever have to cry
Their tears are different too—

More shiny, somehow, and more sad,
You hold your breath to see
If everything will come out right
And they'll live happily;

If Pierrot will kiss Pierrette
  Beneath an orange moon,
And Harlequin and Columbine
  Outwit old Pantaloon.

You know they will, they always do,
  But still your heart must beat,
And you must pray they will be saved,
  And tremble in your seat.

And then it's over and they bow
  All edged about with light,
The curtain rattles down and shuts
  Them every one from sight.

It's strange to find the afternoon
  Still bright outside the door,
And all the people hurrying by
  The way they were before!

RACHEL LYMAN FIELD.

## BATHTUB BAY

The boats that sail in Nancy's fleet
Are such as never sailed the sea.
Content they lie in Bathtub Bay
(An island there, is Nancy's knee).
The sponge becomes a fishing smack,
The cake of soap, a small canoe,
The bathbrush is a battleship
That sails so proudly on the blue.
There's lots of fun in Bathtub Bay;
So Nancy plays there every day.

LENORE RIGGS.

## FUN IN A GARRET

We're having a lovely time to-day!
We're all of us up in the garret at play!
We have three houses under the eaves—
Not real, you know, but make-believes.
Two we live in, and one is a store,
Where a little old screen makes a truly door.

Warren keeps store, and Joe is his clerk.
And Betty and I stay home and work.
Joe comes around and knocks or rings,
And we order potatoes and steaks and things,
And sometimes we go to the store and buy,
Or send the children for ribbons or pie.

It's lots of fun—just try it some day
When it rains too hard to go out to play.

EMMA C. DOWD.

## FUN ON THE BEACH

We have much sand along our beach.
Lee and Tom and Mary and Top
Come over with spoons and dishes and pails
To make some cakes for our bakery-shop.

Sometimes we make a railroad track—
We make the tunnels and signals too,
So the passenger trains and those with freight
Can have the chance to go right through.

Sometimes we make a great big lake.
We build great piers and smaller docks.
The boats we have are large and small.
The large ones sometimes hit the rocks!

Sometimes we all work hard and dig.
We bury Tom in a great big hole.
He humps his back and then comes out,
To get washed off when the big waves roll!

ALICE WILKINS.

## HOW THE KITE LEARNED TO FLY

"I never can do it," the little kite said,
As he looked at the others high over his head;
"I know I should fall if I tried to fly."
"Try," said the big kite; "only try,
Or I fear you never will learn at all."
But the little kite said, "I'm afraid I'll fall."

The big kite nodded: "Ah, well, good-by;
I'm off"; and he rose toward the tranquil sky.
Then the little kite's paper stirred at the sight,
And trembling he shook himself free for flight.
First whirling and frightened, then braver grown,
Up, up he rose through the air alone,
Till the big kite looking down could see
The little one rising steadily.

Then how the little kite thrilled with pride,
As he sailed with the big kite side by side!
While far below he could see the ground,
And the boys like small spots moving round.
They rested high in the quiet air,
And only the birds and clouds were there.
"Oh, how happy I am!" the little kite cried,
"And all because I was brave and tried."

UNKNOWN.

I took my dolly for a walk.
  Before we reached the gate,
She kicked her little slipper off,
  And soon she lost the mate.

I took my dolly for a ride.
  It was a windy day.
She broke her pretty parasol,
  And her bonnet blew away.

I took my dolly for a sail
  And what did dolly do,
But drop her necklace overboard.
  It was her best one, too.

The more and more I scolded her,
  The more and more she smiled.
Now would you take her out again?
  She's such a naughty child.

UNKNOWN.

## KITE TALES

My kite grabbed on a gusty gale
  And took a wild and windy sail.

I held on tight while it flew far
  To where the elves and fairies are.

And when I drew it back to me
  It told of things I'd like to see;

And if you'll listen I'll tell you
  A tale my kite told, maybe two.

Why, one time pussywillows were
  The baby fairies' coats of fur;

And there's a fairy wishing well
  Hid in the ferns of Dingle Dell;

And what you wish in it comes true.
  I wish that I could wish a few.

I'd wish as sure as anything
That all the year were made of spring.

Then I could sail my kite away
For fairy secrets every day.

ROSE WALDO.

## LEARNING TO SKATE

When brother teaches her to skate,
They never stay out very late,
But, oh, it is such fun!
With sister holding fast one hand,
She feels grown-up and much too grand,
To want to skip or run.

She tells them both that she thinks they
Should hurry home from school each day,—
For it gets dark so soon—
And take her to the meadow pond,
Or to the river just beyond,
To skate each afternoon.

Her skating lessons are a game,
That you might call by any name—
In frosty winter air,
The wind gives her a little ride
With brother laughing at her side,
The Ice King everywhere!

EMILIE BLACKMORE STAPP.

## MONDAY MORNING

In the tub on Monday morning
All my dolly's dresses go;
There they dance among the bubbles
Till they're white as snow.

When I squeeze the water out
And hang them up to dry,
They wave their arms excitedly
To people passing by.

HELEN WING.

## MUD CAKES

*(A Good Recipe)*

Some water—about a half a cup—
And two full cups of earth,
Mix well and beat and beat and beat
For all that you are worth:
Roll out and cut a half inch thick—
A dozen or so 'twill make,
Then arrange them on a board
And set in sun to bake!

### FROSTING

A cup of sand, the white is best,
Add water drop by drop
Until enough to mix and spread
All over each cake top!
In center stick a big, fat plum
Or a berry or a cherry meat
And then you'll have some little cakes
That *look* good enough to eat!

MILDRED D. SHACKLETT.

## MY KITE

The busy wind is out today
A-blowing all the clouds away
And chasing butterflies and bees
And making music in the trees.

My kite it carries far and high
Till it is lost up in the sky.

BEATRICE BROWN.

## ON THE BEACH

When summer comes I like to stay
Down on the beach, where I can play
Close by the blue and shining sea,
That brings the singing shells to me.

Sometimes big ships go sailing by,
And then you hear the sea-gulls cry;
When bell-buoys ring is it the rule
For fish to start at once for school?

The waves come dancing full of fun
To play with me—then back they run;
Perhaps they hear their mother call,
And so—they do not stay at all.

The waves are just like children, who
Are happy as they run to you;
Their mother is the sea, I know,
For home to her they always go!

EMILIE BLACKMORE STAPP.

## ROLLER SKATES

Rumble, rumble, rumble, goes the gloomy "L"
And the street car rattles as well,
Motor-trucks wheeze and limousines purr,
Everything is noisy—all the world's astir!
Bang-whirr, bang-whirr, we'll all join too,
The pavement may be dirty, but the sky's clean blue!

Whiz by the lady with the funny little girl,
Swing around the corner in a gleeful whirl!
Don't bump the fat man, jump the other way,
Yell a little, shout a little, "Hip-hooray!"
Everybody's busy—we'll be busy too,
The pavements may be dirty, but the sky's clean blue.

JOHN FARRAR.

## SPINNING TOP

When I spin round without a stop
And keep my balance like a top,
I find that soon the floor will swim
Before my eyes; and then, like him,
I lie all dizzy on the floor
Until I feel like spinning more.

FRANK DEMPSTER SHERMAN.

## TAKING TURNS

We like to go to Granny's house
And spend a happy day;
Where cooky jars are always full
It is such fun to stay.

Her garden now is bright with flowers,
The honey bees are there,
And from her trees the singing birds
Are flying everywhere.

Back in the barn our pony waits,
With Rover at his side,
When brother leads the pony out,
He gives us each a ride.

Then Rover barks and runs ahead,
Down to the shady lane,

Oh, taking turns is fine—for soon
Our turns come round again.

EMILIE BLACKMORE STAPP.

## THE BIG ARM-CHAIR

The big arm-chair by the warm fireside
  Is a wonderful chair, you know;
It is thousands and thousands of magic things
  In the dusk, with the fire aglow.

Sometimes it's a ship, with a great tall mast,
  And I am the captain bold;
I rove the seas with a pirate crew,
  In our quest for hidden gold.

Sometimes it's a grim old castle of stone,
  With a loophole here and there,
With a moat *that* deep, and a donjon keep,
  And a round tower high in the air.

Sometimes it's a beautiful Arab steed,
  That no one can sit but me,
Or a rocky coral cannibal isle
  In the far-off Southern Sea.

Yet to see it there, like an ordin'ry chair,
  You would never imagine, I know,
That it really was thousands of wonderful things
  In the dusk, with the fire aglow.

E. H. R.

## THE DRUM

The drum's a quiet little fellow
When he's left alone.
But, oh, how he does roar and bellow,
Rattle, snap and groan,

Clatter, spatter, dash and patter,
Rumble, shriek and moan,
Whene'er I take my sticks in hand
And beat him soundly for the band.

JOHN FARRAR.

## THE SWING

How do you like to go up in a swing,
  Up in the air so blue?
Oh, I do think it the pleasantest thing
  Ever a child can do!

Up in the air and over the wall,
  Till I can see so wide,
Rivers and trees and cattle and all
  Over the countryside—

Till I look down on the garden green,
  Down on the roof so brown—
Up in the air I go flying again,
  Up in the air and down!

ROBERT LOUIS STEVENSON.

## THE SWING SHIP

My swing is my airship,
Up so high, I can fly
And see for miles around
The neighbors' plains of different grains
Like a patched quilt on the ground!

Here on the right hand side I see
A chimney poke a line of smoke
From a cottage far, far off—
To the left I look and spy a brook
Like a huge, curved wat'ring trough!

My swing is my airship,
I can fly up so high
But when my hold I yield
Back down I float in my winged boat
To the orchard, my landing field!

MILDRED D. SHACKLETT.

## WALKING

When Daddy
Walks
With Jean and me,
We have a
Lot of fun
'Cause we can't
Walk as fast
As he,
Unless we
Skip and
Run!
I stretch,
And stretch
My legs so far,
I nearly slip
And fall—
But how
Does Daddy
Take such steps?
He doesn't stretch
At all!

GRACE GLAUBITZ.

## A DISCOVERY

Oh! such a funny thing I found
A-crawling slowly on the ground.

Its legs and head and things like that
Were worn just underneath its hat.
And it was much afraid of me
Because, as quick as quick could be,
It pulled its legs in out of sight
And shut its head and tail up tight.
It stayed quite still till Mother came
Who said that "Turtle" was its name.
And that it lived inside its shell
Though what it ate she couldn't tell
And laughed because I said a mouse
Would die in such a stuffy house.

ARTHUR A. KNIPE.

## A FRIEND IN THE GARDEN

He is not John the gardener,
  And yet the whole day long
Employs himself most usefully,
  The flower beds among.

He is not Tom the pussy-cat,
  And yet the other day,
With stealthy stride and glistening eye,
  He crept upon his prey.

He is not Dash the dear old dog,
  And yet, perhaps, if you
Took pains with him and petted him,
  You'd come to love him too.

He's not a Blackbird, though he chirps,
  And though he once was black;
And now he wears a loose, gray coat,
  All wrinkled on the back.

He's got a very dirty face,
  And very shining eyes;

He sometimes comes and sit indoors;
He looks—and p'r'aps is—wise.

But in a sunny flower bed
He has his fixed abode;
He eats the things that eat my plants—
He is a friendly *toad*.

JULIANA H. EWING.

## A LITTLE FROG

A little frog sat on a log
That lay out in the sun.
He had to dive and swim to shore,
Because he couldn't run!

ALICE WILKINS.

## A RABBIT

A rabbit works its ears, and tries
To watch you with its rabbit eyes;
Its saucy tail it flounces,
And when it hits the ground, it bounces.

MARY CAROLYN DAVIES.

## AN OLD RAT'S TALE

He was a rat, and she was a rat,
And down in one hole they did dwell;
And both were as black as a witch's cat,
And they loved each other well.

He had a tail and she had a tail,
Both long and curling and fine;
And each said, "Yours is the finest tail
In the world excepting mine."

He smelt the cheese, and she smelt the cheese,
  And they both pronounced it good;
And both remarked it would greatly add
  To the charms of their daily food.

So he ventured out, and she ventured out,
  And I saw them go with pain;
But what befell them I never can tell,
  For they never came back again.

NURSERY RHYME.

## CATFISH

The catfish with whiskers that lives in the brook
Is an ugly old beast with the wickedest look.
I suppose there were mouse-fish one time in brook town,
Till that ugly old cat-fish gulped all of them down.

JOHN FARRAR.

## FROGS AT SCHOOL

Twenty froggies went to school
Down beside a rushy pool,—
Twenty little coats of green;
Twenty vests all white and clean.
"We must be in time," said they:
"First we study, then we play:
That is how we keep the rule,
Whenever froggies go to school."

Master Bullfrog, grave and stern,
Called the classes in their turn;
Taught them how to nobly strive,
Likewise how to leap and dive;
From his seat upon the log,
Showed them how to say "Ker-chog!"

Also how to dodge a blow
From the sticks that bad boys throw.

Twenty froggies grew up fast;
Bullfrogs they became at last;
Not one dunce among the lot;
Not one lesson they forgot;
Polished in a high degree,
As each froggie ought to be,
Now they sit on other logs,
Teaching other little frogs.

GEO. COOPER.

## HOW CREATURES MOVE

The lion walks on padded paws
The squirrel leaps from limb to limb
While flies can crawl straight up a wall
And seals can dive and swim.
The worm he wiggles all around
The monkey swings by his tail
And birds may hop upon the ground
Or spread their wings and sail.
But boys and girls
Have much more fun;
They leap and dance
And walk and run.

UNKNOWN.

I had a little hobby horse,
  His name was Tommy Gray,
His head was made of peas straw,
  His body made of hay;
I saddled him and bridled him,
  And rode him up to town,
There came a little puff of wind
  And blew him up and down.

NURSERY RHYME.

I had a little pony,
His name was Dapple-gray,
I lent him to a lady,
To ride a mile away;
She whipped him, she lashed him,
She rode him through the mire;
I would not lend my pony now
For all the ladies hire.

NURSERY RHYME.

## I LIKE LITTLE PUSSY

I like little Pussy,
Her coat is so warm;
And if I don't hurt her
She'll do me no harm.
So I'll not pull her tail,
Nor drive her away,
But Pussy and I
Very gently will play;
She shall sit by my side,
And I'll give her some food;
And she'll love me because
I am gentle and good.

I'll pat little Pussy,
And then she will purr,
And thus show her thanks
For my kindness to her;
I'll not pinch her ears,
Nor tread on her paws,
Lest I should provoke her
To use her sharp claws;
I never will vex her,
Nor make her displeased,
For Pussy can't bear
To be worried or teased.

JANE TAYLOR.

## LITTLE BROWN BEAR

Woof! Woof! Woof!
Brown bear—Yum!
Here is honey
Come—eat some!

I know you like it
Because it's good—
Little brown bear,
Living in the wood.

ALICE WILKINS.

## LITTLE CHARLIE CHIPMUNK

Little Charlie Chipmunk was a *talker*. Mercy me!
He chattered after breakfast and he chattered after tea!
He chattered to his father and he chattered to his mother!
He chattered to his sister and he chattered to his brother!
He chattered till his family was almost driven *wild*
Oh, little Charlie Chipmunk was a *very* tiresome child!

HELEN COWLES LECRON.

## LITTLE SNAIL [1]

I saw a snail
Come down the garden walk,
He wagged his head this way . . . that way . . .
Like a clown in a circus.
He looked from side to side
As though he were from a different country.
I have always said he carries his house on his back . . .

[1] *Reprinted by permission from "Poems by a Little Girl." Copyright, 1920, by Frederick A. Stokes Co.*

Today in the rain
I saw that it was his umbrella!

HILDA CONKLING.

## LONG TIME AGO

Once there was a little kitty
Whiter than snow;
In a barn she used to frolic,
Long time ago.

In the barn a little mousie
Ran to and fro;
For she heard the kitty coming,
Long time ago.

Two eyes had little kitty
Black as a sloe;
And they spied the little mousie,
Long time ago.

Four paws had little kitty,
Paws soft as dough;
And they caught the little mousie,
Long time ago.

Nine teeth had little kitty,
All in a row;
And they bit the little mousie,
Long time ago.

When the teeth bit little mousie,
Little mouse cried, "Oh!"
But she got away from kitty,
Long time ago.

ELIZABETH PRENTISS.

## MARY'S LAMB

Mary had a little lamb,
  Its fleece was white as snow;
And everywhere that Mary went,
  The lamb was sure to go.

He followed her to school one day,
  Which was against the rule;
It made the children laugh and play
  To see a lamb at school.

And so the teacher turned him out,
  But still he lingered near,
And waited patiently about
  Till Mary did appear.

"What makes the lamb love Mary so?"
  The eager children cried.
"Oh, Mary loves the lamb, you know,"
  The teacher then replied.

SARAH J. HALE

## MILKING TIME [1]

When the cows come home the milk is coming;
Honey's made while the bees are humming;
Duck and drake on the rushy lake,
And the deer live safe in the breezy brake;
And timid, pert little bunny
Winks his nose, and sits all sunny.

CHRISTINA ROSSETTI.

[1] *From "Sing Song." By permission of the Macmillan Co.*

## MY AIREDALE DOG

I have a funny Airedale dog,
He's just about my size,
With such a serious-looking face,
And eyes that seem so wise.

He looks as if he'd like to laugh,
But yet his long, straight muzzle
Gives him a kind of solemn look—
He surely is a puzzle.

And he is just as full of tricks
As any dog could be,
And we have mighty jolly times
Because he plays with me,

And never tries to bite or snap;
He doesn't even whine,—
And that is why my Airedale dog
Is such a friend of mine.

W. L. MASON.

## MY LITTLE NEIGHBOR

My little neighbor's table's set,
And slyly he comes down the tree,
His feet firm in each tiny fret
The bark has fashioned cunningly.

He pauses on a favorite knot;
Beneath the oak his feast is spread;
He asks no friend to share his lot,
Or dine with him on acorn bread.

He keeps his whiskers trim and neat,
His tail with care he brushes through;

He runs about on all four feet—
When dining he sits up on two.

He has the latest stripe in furs,
And wears them all the year round;
He does not mind the prick of burrs
Where there are chestnuts to be found.

I watch his home and guard his store,
A cozy hollow tree;
He often sits within his door,
And chatters wond'rous things to me.

MARY AUGUSTA MASON.

## MY PONY

My pony toss'd his sprightly head,
And would have smiled, if smile he could,
To thank me for the slice of bread
He thinks so delicate and good;
His eyes are very bright and wild,
He looks as if he loved me so,
Although I only am a child
And he's a real horse you know.

How charming it would be to rear,
And have hind legs to balance on;
Of hay and oats within a year
To leisurely devour a ton;
To stoop my head and quench my drought
With water in a lovely pail;
To wear a snaffle in my mouth,
Fling back my ears, and slash my tail!

To gallop madly round a field,—
Who tries to catch me is a goose,
And then with dignity to yield
My stately back for riders' use;

To feel as only horses can,
  When matters take their proper course,
And no one notices the man,
  While loud applauses greet the horse!

He canters fast or ambles slow,
  And either is a pretty game;
His duties are but pleasures—oh,
  I wish that mine were just the same!
Lessons would be another thing
  If I might turn from book and scroll,
And learn to gallop round a ring,
  As he did when a little foal.

It must be charming to be shod,
  And beautiful beyond my praise,
When tired of rolling on the sod,
  To stand upon all-fours and graze!
Alas! my dreams are weak and wild,
  I must not ape my betters so;
Alas! I only am a child,
  And he's a real horse you know.

"A."

## OUR CIRCUS

We had a circus in our shed
(Admission, three new pins a head)
And every girl and boy I know
Is talking yet about our show.

They laughed so hard at Fatty Brown
When he came out to be the clown,
That all the neighbors ran to see
Whatever such a noise could be.

Our tin-pan and mouth-organ band
Played tunes that sounded simply grand;

We had a truly sawdust ring,
Pink lemonade, 'n everything.

The big menagerie was nice:
Three cats, one dog, and five white mice,
A parrot that Bill's uncle lent;
All underneath a bedspread tent.

Then Ned and Buster took a sheet
That covered them from head to feet
And made a horse that kicked and pranced
And when it heard the band, it danced.

And Sally Ann was "Bareback Queen!"
No finer rider could be seen;
She stood right up, and looked so proud,
But kissed her hand to all the crowd.

We took some chalk—blue, green, and red—
And made a "Tattooed Man" of Fred;
Jim juggled lighted cigarettes,
And Tom turned double somersets.

We had tall stilts—and flying rings—
And lots and lots of other things—
And every boy and girl I know
Said yes, it was a *dandy* show!

LAURA LEE RANDALL.

## OVER IN THE MEADOW

Over in the meadow,
In the sand, in the sun,
Lived an old mother toad and
And her little toadie one.
"Wink!" said the mother;
"I wink," said the one:

So she winked and she blinked
  In the sand, in the sun.

Over in the meadow,
  Where the stream runs blue,
Lived an old mother fish
  And her little fishes two.
"Swim!" said the mother;
  "We swim," said the two:
So they swam and they leaped
  Where the stream runs blue.

Over in the meadow,
  In a hole in a tree,
Lived a mother bluebird
  And her little birdies three;
"Sing!" said the mother;
  "We sing," said the three:
So they sang, and were glad,
  In the hole in the tree.

OLIVE A. WADSWORTH.
(Katherine Floyd Dana.)

## PUSSYCAT MOLE

Pussycat mole jumped over a coal,
  And in her best petticoat burnt a big hole.
Poor pussy's weeping, she'll get no more milk
  Until her best petticoat's mended with silk.

NURSERY RHYME.

## SALLY CENTIPEDE

A very careless child indeed
Is little Sally Centipede—
On this her friends are all agreed
  When they have heard the news!

Her actions make her father sigh,
And make her mother almost cry,
While Grandma murmurs, "Fie, oh, fie!"
  *For Sally scuffs her shoes!*

The family is large, I've heard,
And Sally's father, I've inferred,
Is far from wealthy, yet—my word!
  This foolish little dunce
Just scuffs and scuffs each fifty pair
That Father brings her home to wear!
They all look horrid, I declare,
  When she has worn them once!

If you, my dear, had all the feet
That Sally has, and I should meet
You walking down this busy street,
  I'm very sure indeed
That all your hundred shoes would shine
Like mirrors, and would look as fine
And new and bright and smooth as mine!
  (Not like Sal Centipede!)

HELEN COWLES LECRON.

## SNAIL

Everybody nowadays
  Seems in such a hurry;
The world is most too swift for me
  Still I never worry.
Independent, slow but sure,
  I travel on my way;
My home I carry on my back
  I have no rent to pay.

C. LINDSAY MC COY.

## THE ARMADILLO

The armadillo roams the far
Off plains of South America.
He wears a bony suit of mail
That covers him from head to tail.
I do not think an armadillo
Would make a very "comfy" pillow.

LESLEY GORDON.

## THE CAT

The pussy that climbs to the top of the tree
Is really much shorter and thinner than me;
And yet though I try all the whole summer through,
I cannot do half of the things she can do.

She's only as old as my new baby brother,
And yet she can run as fast as her mother;
It's funny some people are as clever as that:
I wish I were only as nice as the cat!

HELEN HAY WHITNEY.

## THE CIRCUS

Friday came and the circus was there
And mother said that the twins and I
And Charles and Clarence and all of us
Could go and see the parade go by.

And there were wagons with pictures on
And you never could guess what they had inside
Nobody could guess, for the doors were shut
And there was a dog that a monkey could ride.

A man on the top of a sort of a cart
Was clapping his hands and making a talk.
And the elephant came—he can step pretty far—
It made us laugh to see him walk.

Three beautiful ladies came riding by.
And each one had on a golden dress,
And each one had a golden whip.
They were queens of Sheba, I guess.

A big wild man was in a cage,
And he had some snakes going over his feet.
And somebody said, "He eats them alive!"
But I didn't see him eat.

ELIZABETH MADOX ROBERTS.

## THE CIRCUS PARADE [1]

Tomorrow, tomorrow's the circus parade!
Just think what I shall see!
What crowds of people in gay colored clothes
All lined up the street there will be.

And some of the children will have red balloons,
As up by the curbing they stand,
Then off in the distance we'll suddenly hear
The circus's big brass band!

Behind the crash bang! of the music they play,
Come riders in red velvet gowns,
And after them doing the funniest things,
A silly procession of clowns.

Then lions and tigers that pace up and down,
In wagons all painted with gold,
And monkeys a-playing just all kinds of tricks,
As they grimace and chatter and scold.

[1] *From "My Bookhouse" with the permission of the author and* THE BOOK HOUSE FOR CHILDREN.

Oh, next there come camels and elephants, too,
With men on their backs astride,
And queer little ponies, no bigger than dogs,
And a donkey perhaps beside!

And then there come chariots rumbling by
With horses all four in a row;
And the wheezing, old calliope is
The very tail end of the show!

OLIVE BEAUPRÉ MILLER.

## THE COW

The friendly cow all red and white,
I love with all my heart:
She gives me cream with all her might,
To eat with apple-tart.

She wanders lowing here and there,
And yet she cannot stray,
All in the pleasant open air,
The pleasant light of day;

And blown by all the winds that pass
And wet with all the showers,
She walks among the meadow grass
And eats the meadow flowers.

ROBERT LOUIS STEVENSON.

## THE CROCODILE

How doth the little crocodile
Improve his shining tail,
And pour the waters of the Nile
On every golden scale!

How cheerfully he seems to grin
  How neatly spreads his claws,
And welcomes little fishes in
  With gently smiling jaws.

UNKNOWN.

## THE DUCK AND THE KANGAROO

Said the Duck to the Kangaroo,
  "Good gracious! how you hop
Over the fields, and the water too,
  As if you never would stop!
My life is a bore in this nasty pond;
And I long to go out in the world beyond:
  I wish I could hop like you,"
  Said the Duck to the Kangaroo.

"Please give me a ride on your back,"
  Said the Duck to the Kangaroo:
"I would sit quite still, and say nothing but 'Quack'
  The whole of the long day through;
And we'd go to the Dee, and the Jelly Bo Lee,
Over the land and over the sea:
  Please take me to ride! oh, do!"
  Said the Duck to the Kangaroo.

Said the Kangaroo to the Duck,
  "This requires some little reflection.
Perhaps, on the whole, it might bring me luck:
  And there seems but one objection;
Which is, if you'll let me speak so bold,
Your feet are unpleasantly wet and cold,
  And would probably give me roo-
  Matiz," said the Kangaroo.

Said the Duck, "As I sat on the rocks,
  I have thought over that completely;

And I bought four pairs of worsted socks,
Which fit my web feet neatly;
And, to keep out the cold, I've bought a cloak;
And every day a cigar I'll smoke;
All to follow my own dear true
Love of a Kangaroo."

Said the Kangaroo, "I'm ready,
All in the moonlight pale;
But to balance me well, dear Duck, sit steady,
And quite at the end of my tail."
So away they went with a hop and a bound;
And they hopped the whole world three times round.
And who so happy, oh! who,
As the Duck and the Kangaroo?

EDWARD LEAR.

## THE DUEL

The gingham dog and the calico cat
Side by side on the table sat;
'Twas half twelve, and (what do you think!)
Nor one nor t'other had slept a wink!
The old Dutch clock and the Chinese plate
Appeared to know as sure as fate
There was going to be a terrible spat.
*(I wasn't there; I simply state*
*What was told to me by the Chinese plate!)*

The gingham dog went "Bow-wow-wow!"
And the calico cat replied "Mee-ow!"
The air was littered, an hour or so,
With bits of gingham and calico,
While the old Dutch clock in the chimney place
Up with its hands before its face,
For it always dreaded a family row!
*(Now mind: I'm telling you*
*What the old Dutch clock declares is true!)*

The Chinese plate looked very blue,
And wailed, "Oh, dear! what shall we do!"
But the gingham dog and the calico cat
Wallowed this way and tumbled that,
  Employing every tooth and claw
  In the awfullest way you ever saw—
And, oh! how the gingham and calico flew!
  (*Don't fancy I exaggerate—*
  *I got my news from the Chinese plate!*)

Next morning, where the two had sat
They found no trace of dog or cat:
And some folks think unto this day
That burglars stole that pair away!
  But the truth about the cat and pup
  Is this: they ate each other up!
Now what do you really think of that!
  (*The old Dutch clock, it told me so,*
  *And that is how I came to know.*)

EUGENE FIELD.

## THE ELEPHANT[1]

The elephant is very large
And clumsy as a wooden barge,
With legs like tree-trunks, yet he's mild
And gentle as a little child.

The elephant walks far away
And sees strange children in their play,
And carries logs and iron bars
As easily as motor-cars.

[1] *Reprinted by permission from "For Days and Days: A Year-round Treasury of Verse for Children," by Annette Wynne. Copyright, 1919, by Frederick A. Stokes Co.*

The elephant's a great big beast—
Not beautiful, but good, at least,
Strong as a tree, but withal mild
And gentle as a little child.

ANNETTE WYNNE.

## THE ELEPHANT'S TRUNK

The elephant always carries his trunk.
I couldn't do that with my own.
His trunk is a part of himself, you see—
It's part of his head—it's grown!

ALICE WILKINS.

The finest, biggest fish, you see,
Will be the one that's caught by me;
But if the big fish will not bite,
Why, then I'll catch a little mite.

NURSERY RHYME.

## THE FISHING-POLE

A fishing-pole's a curious thing;
It's made of just a stick and string;
A boy at one end and a wish,
And on the other end a fish.

MARY CAROLYN DAVIES.

## THE FOX

The Fox set out in a hungry plight,
And begged the moon to give him light,
For he'd many a mile to travel that night.
Before he could reach his den O!

First he came to a farmer's yard,
  Where the ducks and the geese declared it was hard
That their nerves should be shaken, and their rest be marred
  By a visit from Mr. Fox O!

He seized the gray goose by the sleeve,
  Says he, "Madam Gray Goose, by your leave,
I'll carry you off without reprieve,
  And take you away to my den O!"

He seized the gray duck by the neck,
  And flung her across his back,
While the old duck cried out, "Quack, quack, quack,"
  With her legs dangling down behind O!

Then old Mrs. Flipper Flapper jumped out of bed,
  And out of the window she popped her head,
Crying, "John, John, John, the gray goose is gone,
  And the fox is off to his den O!"

Then John went up to the top of the hill,
  And he blew a blast both loud and shrill.
Says the Fox, "That is fine music, still
  I'd rather be off to my den O!"

So the Fox he hurried off to his den,
  To his dear little foxes eight, nine, ten.
Says he, "We're in luck, here's a big fat duck
  With her legs dangling down behind O!"

Then the Fox sat down with his hungry wife,
  And they made a good meal without fork or knife.
They never had a better time in all their life,
  And the little ones picked the bones O!

OLD RHYME.

## THE HAPPY SHEEP

All through the night the happy sheep
Lie in the meadow grass asleep.

Their wool keeps out the frost and rain
Until the sun comes round again.

They have no buttons to undo,
Nor hair to brush like me and you,

And with the light they lift their heads
To find their breakfast on their beds

Or rise and walk about and eat
The carpet underneath their feet.

WILFRED THORLEY.

## THE HIPPOPOTAMUS

In the squdgy river,
   Down the oozely bank,
Where the ripples shiver,
   And the reeds are rank.

Where the purple Kippo
   Makes an awful fuss,
Lives the hip-hip-hippo
   Hippo-pot-a-mus!

Broad his back and steady;
   Broad and flat his nose;
Sharp and keen and ready
   Little eyes are those.

You would think him dreaming
   Where the mud is deep.

It is only seeming—
He is not asleep.

Better not disturb him,
There'd be an awful fuss
If you touched the Hippo,
Hippo-pot-a-mus.

GEORGIA R. DURSTON.

## THE HORSES OF THE SEA[1]

The horses of the sea
Rear a foaming crest,
But the horses of the land
Serve us the best.

The horses of the land
Munch corn and clover,
While the foaming sea-horses
Toss and turn over.

CHRISTINA ROSSETTI.

## THE LITTLE KITTENS

"Where are you going, my little kittens?"
"We are going to town to get us some mittens."
"What! Mittens for kittens!
Do kittens wear mittens?
Who ever saw little kittens with mittens?"

"Where are you going, my little cat?"
"I am going to town to get me a hat."
"What! A hat for a cat!
A cat get a hat!
Who ever saw a cat with a hat?"

[1] *From "Sing Song." By permission of the Macmillan Co.*

"Where are you going, my little pig?"
"I am going to town to get me a wig."
  "What! A wig for a pig!
  A pig in a wig!
Who ever saw a pig in a wig?"

ELIZA LEE FOLLEN.

## THE LITTLE TURTLE [1]

There was a little turtle,
He lived in a box.
He swam in a puddle,
He climbed on the rocks.

He snapped at a mosquito,
He snapped at a flea,
He snapped at a minnow,
He snapped at me.

He caught the mosquito,
He caught the flea,
He caught the minnow,
But he didn't catch me.

VACHEL LINDSAY.

## THE MOLE

The burrowing mole lives under the ground
Day in and day out, all the changing year round;
Like a train in a tunnel, in darkness he goes,
And makes his own track with his feet and his nose.

He lives upon worms as content as can be
For breakfast and supper, for dinner and tea,
Yes, just as they are, as a matter of course,
He gobbles them up without cooking or sauce.

[1] *From "Collected Poems." By permission of the Macmillan Co.*

If you lived where he does, in a very short time
I fear you'd be covered completely with grime;
But though he works hard all day long for his meat
And has but one coat, he is perfectly neat.

It's not very often he visits the light,
Except when he's angry and anxious to fight;
Then he and his enemy leave their dark holes,
And in warfare there's nothing more savage than moles.

Their virtues are great, but their tempers are bad,
Biting and scratching, they scuffle like mad,
And over and over they roll in the ditch,
Until it's a puzzle to see which is which.

But if they discover you watching the fray,
They leave off at once to get out of the way,
And burrow so quickly, scarce making a sound,
That before you count ten they're gone into the ground.

EDITH KING.

## THE OWL AND THE PUSSY-CAT

The Owl and the Pussy-Cat went to sea
In a beautiful pea-green boat:
They took some honey, and plenty of money
Wrapped in a five-pound note.
The Owl looked up to the stars above,
And sang to a small guitar,
"O lovely Pussy, O Pussy, my love,
What a beautiful Pussy you are,
You are,
You are!
What a beautiful Pussy you are!"

Pussy said to the Owl, "You elegant fowl,
How charmingly sweet you sing!

Oh! let us be married; too long we have tarried:
  But what shall we do for a ring?"
They sailed away, for a year and a day,
  To the land where the bong-tree grows;
And there in the wood a Piggy-wig stood,
  With a ring at the end of his nose,
        His nose,
        His nose,
  With a ring at the end of his nose.

"Dear Pig, are you willing to sell for one shilling
  Your ring?" Said the Piggy, "I will."
So they took it away, and were married next day
  By the Turkey who lives on the hill.
They dined on mince and slices of quince,
  Which they ate with a runcible spoon;
And hand in hand, on the edge of the sand,
  They danced by the light of the moon,
        The moon,
        The moon,
  They danced by the light of the moon.

EDWARD LEAR.

## THE RABBIT

Brown bunny sits inside his burrow
Till everything is still,
Then out he slips along the furrow,
Or up the grassy hill.

He nibbles all about the bushes
Or sits to wash his face—
But at a sound he stamps and rushes
At a surprising pace—

You see some little streaks and flashes—
A last sharp twink of white

As down his hidy-hole he dashes—
And disappears from sight.

EDITH KING.

## THE RABBIT

The rabbit has a habit
  Of sitting on his heels
With his little paws in front of him;
  I wonder how it feels.

The grasses where he passes
  He nibbles if they suit,
And he nips the tips of daisies,
  Or he chews a tender root.

He rolics and he frolics
  In a very cunning way;
When the moon shines white upon him;
  But he loves to sleep by day.

His hole is where the mole is:
  Down beneath the maple tree;
Twisting in and out and round about,
  As safe as it can be.

GEORGIA R. DURSTON.

## THE SNAIL

To grass, or leaf, or fruit, or wall,
The snail sticks close, nor fears to fall,
As if he grew there, house and all
        Together.
Within that house secure he hides,
When danger imminent betides
Of storm, or other harm besides
        Of weather.

Give but his horns the slightest touch,
His self-collecting power is such,
He shrinks into his house with much
Displeasure.
Where'er he dwells, he dwells alone,
Except himself, has chattels none,
Well satisfied to be his own
Whole treasure.

Thus, hermit-like, his life he leads,
Nor partner of his banquet needs,
And if he meets one, only feeds
The faster.
Who seeks him must be worse than blind
(He and his house are so combined),
If, finding it, he fails to find
Its master.

WILLIAM COWPER.

## THE WOLF

When the pale moon hides and the wild wind wails,
And over the tree-tops the nighthawk sails,
The gray wolf sits on the world's far rim,
And howls: and it seems to comfort him.

The wolf is a lonely soul, you see,
No beast in the wood, nor bird in the tree,
But shuns his path; in the windy gloom
They give him plenty, and plenty of room.

So he sits with his long, lean face to the sky
Watching the ragged clouds go by.
There in the night, alone, apart,
Singing the song of his lone, wild heart.

Far away, on the world's dark rim
He howls, and it seems to comfort him.

GEORGIA R. DURSTON.

There's a hole in the fence,
  And the rabbits creep through,
And deep in the orchard
  They sup in the dew;
But when I creep down
  At the close of the day
As silent as moonbeams
  They hurry away.

DOROTHY DICKINSON.

*By permission of Boosey & Co., Ltd., from Wonder Book.*

## THREE LITTLE KITTENS

Three little kittens lost their mittens;
  And they began to cry,
    "Oh, mother, dear,
    We very much fear
  That we have lost our mittens."
    "Lost your mittens!
    You naughty kittens!
  Then you shall have no pie."
      "Mee-ow, mee-ow, mee-ow."
  "No, you shall have no pie."

The three little kittens found their mittens;
  And they began to cry,
    "Oh, mother, dear,
    See here, see here!
  See, we have found our mittens!"
    "Put on your mittens,
    You silly kittens,
  And you may have some pie."
      "Purr-r, purr-r, purr-r.
  Oh, let us have the pie!
      Purr-r, purr-r, purr-r."

The three little kittens put on their mittens,
And soon ate up the pie;
"Oh, mother, dear,
We greatly fear
That we have soiled our mittens!"
"Soiled your mittens!
You naughty kittens!"
Then they began to sigh,
"Mee-ow, mee-ow, mee-ow."
Then they began to sigh,
"Mee-ow, mee-ow, mee-ow."

The three little kittens washed their mittens,
And hung them out to dry;
"Oh, mother, dear,
Do not you hear
That we have washed our mittens?"
"Washed your mittens!
Oh, you're good kittens!
But I smell a rat close by,
Hush, hush! Mee-ow, mee-ow."
"We smell a rat close by,
Mee-ow, mee-ow, mee-ow."

ELIZA LEE FOLLEN.

## TIP-TOE TALE

A fish took a notion
To come from his ocean
And take in the sights of the town.
So he bought him a hat
And a coat and cravat
And a one legg-ed trouser of brown! *He did!*
A one legg-ed trouser of brown!

His suit fit so queerly
That everyone nearly

Went following out on the street!
But the best of it all
Was how handsome and tall
He could walk when he didn't have feet! *He did!*
He walked when he didn't have feet!

Now I must confess that
I surely could guess that
A fish trying walking would fail
But with no one's advice
He walked *perfectly* nice
On the very tip-toes of his tail! *He did!*
On the very tip-toes of his tail!

DIXIE WILLSON.

## 'TIS MARCH

'Tis March, and the wriggly earthworms
Are crawling all about
To loosen all the soil and help
The busy farmer out.

For months the squirrel's slumbered
Deep in a hollow tree;
But soon, upon a leafy branch
His summer's nest you'll see.

The turtle's left his mud bed,
And, should you care to look,
You'll find him swimming happily
Within the meadow brook.

The badger and the gopher
Up from their burrows creep,
And, in the sunshine, bright and warm,
Forget their winter sleep.

The frogs and toads are hunting
  Insects, their daily fare.
Look in the trees for tree toads;
  You'll surely find them there.

HOPE NELSON.

## TRACKS

I wonder where the rabbits go
Who leave their tracks across the snow;
For when I follow to their den
The tracks always start out again.

JOHN FARRAR.

## TURTLE TOWN

To-day as I went down the road
I met a terrapin,
And he politely tipped his hat
And grinned a friendly grin.

"Good morning, little boy," he said,
"Good morning and Good day,
I want to go to Turtle Town
And I have lost my way.

"If you will please direct me there
And get me headed straight,
I'll thank you six or seven times
(And even make it eight)."

I told him it was North or South
Or maybe, East or West,
And I suggested that he choose
The road he liked the best.

He listened with such gratitude
A tear came in his voice.
"How very kind you are," he said,
"To give me such a choice!

"You see my richest relatives
All live in Turtle Town,
And Uncle Terry wrote last year
Suggesting I come down.

"And so I left that very hour
(I didn't stop to write);
I've traveled all of every day
And half of every night.

"I wish you might have seen me
When I started on this trip,
(My spats as white as bottled milk,
My gloves without a rip.)

"I wore a purple silk cravat,
My vest was checkered green.
(I had my tailor fit it tight
As skin upon a bean.)

"My figure had the rounded curves
Of some high magistrate,
But with these months of exercise
I've greatly lost in weight.

"My shoes have even worn so thin
There's not the slightest doubt
If I don't get another pair
My toes will soon be out.

"And yet," he said, "I may as well
Go on another year.
If Uncle didn't hear from me
Perhaps he'd think it queer.

"So thank you once or twice again
For being so polite,
And when you come to Turtle Town
*Do* plan to spend the night."

And then he left at such a pace
That if he perseveres
He'll surely get to Turtle Town
Within the next two years.

HELEN WING.

## WAYS OF TRAVELING

Little Mister Polliwog,
You swim to and fro.
When you turn into a frog
You'll hop where'er you go.

ALICE WILKINS.

## WHISKY FRISKY

Whisky Frisky,
Hippity Hop,
Up he goes
To the tree top!

Whirly, Twirly,
Round and round,
Down he scampers
To the ground.

Furly Curly
What a tail!
Tall as a feather
Broad as a sail!

Where's his supper?
In the shell,
Snappy, cracky,
Out it fell!

UNKNOWN.

## WILLIE WOLF

Willie Wolf *will* gulp his food,
Though his mother calls him rude,
Though his brother hides his eyes,
And his sister almost cries.
('Course she knows that crying's silly,
But she's so ashamed of Willie!)
Oh, the dreadful bites he takes
When he's eating pies and cakes!
I should hate to have to see him,
But I'd hate far worse to *be* him!

HELEN COWLES LECRON.

## BLUEBIRD [1]

So happy the song he sings
On the apple-blossom bough!
Remembering how the sun
Melted the long winter snow.
He is the first to come,
He and his comrade, robin,
In his heart joyful
Over returning Spring.
So happy the song he sings
On the apple-blossom bough!

HILDA CONKLING.

[1] *Reprinted by permission from "Shoes of the Wind." Copyright, 1922, by Frederick A. Stokes Co.*

## CHANTICLEER

High and proud on the barnyard fence
Walks rooster in the morning.
He shakes his comb, he shakes his tail
And gives his daily warning.

Get up, you lazy boys and girls,
It's time you should be dressing.
I wonder if he keeps a clock,
Or is he only guessing?

JOHN FARRAR.

## CHICKADEE

I'm as friendly as can be,
And if you'll drop a crumb
Upon your window, Chickadee
Will surely, surely come.

MARION MITCHELL WALKER.

## FIVE LITTLE CHICKENS

Said the first little chicken,
With a queer little squirm,
"Oh, I wish I could find
A fat little worm!"

Said the next little chicken,
With an odd little shrug,
"Oh, I wish I could find
A fat little bug!"

Said the third little chicken,
With a sharp little squeal,
"Oh, I wish I could find
Some nice yellow meal!"

Said the fourth little chicken,
With a small sigh of grief,
"Oh, I wish I could find
A green little leaf!"

Said the fifth little chicken,
With a faint little moan,
"Oh, I wish I could find
A wee gravel-stone!"

"Now, see here," said the mother,
From the green garden-patch,
"If you want any breakfast,
You must come and scratch."

OLD VERSE.

## HONEST MR. ROBIN

Robin rents a tree-top house;
Pays his rent by working, too!
See, he's eating insects there
So there will be fruit for you!

ELEANOR HAMMOND.

## LITTLE ROBIN REDBREAST

Little Robin Redbreast sat upon a tree,
Up went pussy-cat, and down went he;
Down came pussy-cat, and away Robin ran;
Said little Robin Redbreast, "Catch me if you can."

Little Robin Redbreast jumped upon a wall,
Pussy-cat jumped after him, and almost had a fall;
Little Robin chirped and sang, and what did pussy say?
Pussy-cat said naught but "Mew," and Robin flew away.

OLD RHYME.

## MEADOW LARK

My throat is of gold, with a pretty black crescent,
  Folks call me a beautiful bird;
My voice is like silver—so liquid and pleasant,
  The sweetest you ever have heard.

MARION MITCHELL WALKER.

Once I saw a little bird
  Come hop, hop, hop;
So I cried, "Little bird,
  Will you stop, stop, stop?"
And was going to the window
  To say, "How do you do?"
But he shook his little tail,
  And far away he flew.

NURSERY RHYME.

## ORIOLE

See my pretty little nest,
  Built of bits of string;
When the breezes whisper near,
  You should see it swing!
There are four wee babies there,
  In that silken cradle,
They'll sing grown-up Oriole songs,
  Soon as they are able.

MARION MITCHELL WALKER.

## ROBERT OF LINCOLN

Merrily swinging on brier and weed,
  Near to the nest of his little dame,
Over the mountain-side or mead,
  Robert of Lincoln is telling his name:

Bob-o'-link, bob-o'-link,
Spink, spank, spink;
Snug and safe is that nest of ours,
Hidden among the summer flowers.
Chee, chee, chee.

Robert of Lincoln is gaily dressed,
Wearing a bright black wedding-coat;
White are his shoulders and white his crest,
Hear him call his merry note:
Bob-o'-link, bob-o'-link,
Spink, spank, spink;
Look, what a nice new coat is mine,
Sure there was never a bird so fine.
Chee, chee, chee.

W. C. BRYANT.

## ROBIN

The feathers on a robin's breast
Fit like a crimson velvet vest.
There is no peacock, anywhere,
That walks with such a prideful air.
Gay as a flag that can't be still
He flutters on the window-sill,
And pecks the crumbs upon my shelf,
So happy just to be himself:
So happy that he has the spring,
In which to fly—in which to sing.
And out on the lawn the other day,
I think—I think, I heard him say,
"I'll strut about, then stop and see
If anybody looks at me."

ANNE BLACKWELL PAYNE.

## SING-TIME

Robin, sing to the rainbow!
Song-thrush, sing to the blue!
Springtime is on the hilltops
And all the world is new!

Winter slipped out through the valley
Where the pink and purple haze is;
And here is April with her arms
A-brimming full of daisies!

ROSE WALDO.

## SINGING

Of speckled eggs the birdie sings—
  And nests among the trees;
The sailor sings of ropes and things
  In ships upon the seas.

The children sing in far Japan,
  The children sing in Spain;
The organ with the organ man
  Is singing in the rain.

ROBERT LOUIS STEVENSON.

## THE BLUEBIRD

I know the song that the bluebird is singing,
Out in the apple tree where he is swinging,
Brave little fellow! the skies may be dreary,
Nothing cares he while his heart is so cheery.

Hark! how the music leaps out from his throat!
Hark! was there ever so merry a note?
Listen awhile, and you'll hear what he's saying,
Up in the apple tree, swinging and swaying:

"Dear little blossoms, down under the snow,
You must be weary of winter, I know;
Hark! while I sing you a message of cheer,
Summer is coming and springtime is here!

"Little white snowdrop, I pray you arise;
Bright yellow crocus, come, open your eyes;
Sweet little violets hid from the cold,
Put on your mantles of purple and gold;
Daffodils, daffodils! say, do you hear?
Summer is coming, and springtime is here!"

EMILY HUNTINGTON MILLER.

## THE CHICKADEE

Piped a tiny voice hard by,
Gay and polite, a cheerful cry,
"Chic-chicadee-dee!" Saucy note
Out of a sound heart and merry throat,
As if it said, "Good day, good sir.
Fine afternoon, old passenger!
Happy to meet you in these places
When January brings new faces!"

RALPH WALDO EMERSON.

## THE DUCK

If I were in a fairy tale
And it were my good luck
To have a wish, I'd choose to be
A lovely snow-white duck.

When she puts off into the pond
And leaves me on the brink,
She wags her stumpy tail at me
And gives a saucy wink,

Which says as plain as words could say
I'm safe as safe can be,
Stay there, or you will drown yourself,
The pond was made for me.

She goes a-sailing to and fro,
Just like a fishing boat,
And steers and paddles all herself,
And never wets her coat.

Then in the water, upside down,
I've often seen her stand,
More neatly than the little boys
Who do it on the land.

And, best of all, her children are
The ducklings, bright as gold
Who swim about the pond with her
And do as they are told.

EDITH KING.

## THE DUCKS

When our ducks waddle to the pond,
They're awkward as awkward can be—
But when they get in the water and swim,
They glide most gracefully.

ALICE WILKINS.

## THE LAND WHERE THE TAFFY BIRDS GROW

There's a lemondrop monkey that whistles and sings
And marshmallow chickens with sugary wings,
Eating wee gumdrop worms that the mother hen brings,
In the Land Where the Taffy Birds Grow.

The rivers are gold-colored honey so sweet,
And a licorice dog, you are certain to meet,
With a lollipop pig that has caramel feet,
  In the Land Where the Taffy Birds Grow.

There's a chocolate mouse and a peppermint cat,
And a sugarplum cow in a cocoanut hat,
Baking cinnamon cookies, so puffy and fat,
  In the Land Where the Taffy Birds Grow.

You'll see round doughnut stars playing peek-a-boo,
And a big yellow moon smiling at you,
(A gingerbread man told me these things were true)
  In the Land Where the Taffy Birds Grow.

MARGARET MC BRIDE HOSS.

## THE LARK

A close gray sky,
And poplars gray and high,
The country-side along;
The steeple hold
Across the acres old—
And then a song!

Oh, far, far, far,
As any spire or star
Beyond the cloistered wall!
Oh, high, high, high,
A heart-throb in the sky—
Then not at all!

LIZETTE WOODWORTH REESE.

## THE LITTLE SHEPHERD'S SONG

*(13th Century)*

The leaves, the little birds, and I,
The fleece clouds and the sweet, sweet sky,
The pages singing as they ride
Down there, down there where the river is wide—
Heigh-o, what a day! What a lovely day!
Even too lovely to hop and play
　　　　With my sheep
　　　　　Or sleep
　　　　In the sun!

And so I lie in the deep, deep grass
And watch the pages as they pass,
And sing to them as they to me
Till they turn the bend by the poplar tree.
And then—O then, I sing right on
To the leaves and the lambs and myself alone!
　　　　For I think there must be
　　　　　Inside of me
　　　　A bird!

WILLIAM ALEXANDER PERCY.

The North Wind doth blow,
And we shall have snow,
And what will the robin do then?
　　　　　　　　Poor thing!

He will sit in a barn,
And keep himself warm,
And hide his head under his wing,
　　　　　　　　Poor thing!

NURSERY RHYME.

## THE ROBIN

When father takes his spade to dig
Then Robin comes along;
He sits upon a little twig
And sings a little song.

Or, if the trees are rather far
He does not stay alone,
But comes up close to where we are
And bobs upon a stone.

LAURENCE ALMA-TADEMA.

## THE SCREECH OWL

The screech owl lives in a hole in a tree.
Only at night is he able to see;
On noiseless wings he flies about
To catch any mice that may be out.
Then he flies back, and sleeps all day
While you and I are out to play.

UNKNOWN.

## THE SEA GULL

I watched the pretty white sea gull
Come riding into town,
The waves came up when he came up,
Went down when he went down.

LEROY JACKSON.

## THE SEA GULL

All day long o'er the ocean I fly,
My white wings beating fast through the sky,

I hunt fishes all down the bay
And ride on rocking billows in play.

All night long in my rock home I rest,
Away up on a cliff is my nest,
The waves murmur, murmur below
And winds fresh from the sea o'er me blow.

GAELIC FOLK-SONG.

## THE WOODPECKER

The woodpecker pecked out a little round hole
And made him a house in the telephone pole.
One day when I watched, he poked out his head
And he had on a hood and a collar of red.

When the streams of rain pour out of the sky,
And the sparkles of lightning go flashing by,
And the big, big wheels of thunder roll,
He can snuggle back in the telephone pole.

ELIZABETH MADOX ROBERTS.

## THERE WAS AN OLD OWL

There was an old owl lived in an oak
  Wisky, wasky, weedle;
And all the words he ever spoke
  Were, "Fiddle, faddle, feedle."

OLD RHYME.

## WELCOME VISITORS

What are you doing out here in the snow
Little birds, little birds, when the winds blow?
Snow may keep falling and winds may blow high,
Still you are happy with children close by.

They bring you crumblings and scatter them here
Little birds, little birds—feathery—dear—
Now you are singing contented and gay,
Have you mistaken the winter for May?

What is the message you came here to bring
Little birds, little birds, calling to Spring?
Tell us again as you sing it once more.
We would be knowing Spring knocks at our door.

EMILIE BLACKMORE STAPP.

## "WHAT DOES LITTLE BIRDIE SAY?"

What does little birdie say,
In her nest at peep of day?
"Let me fly," says little birdie,
"Mother, let me fly away."
"Birdie, rest a little longer,
Till the little wings are stronger."
So she rests a little longer,
Then she flies away.

What does little baby say,
In her bed at peep of day?
Baby says, like little birdie,
"Let me rise and fly away."
"Baby, sleep a little longer,
Till the little limbs are stronger."
If she sleeps a little longer,
Baby too shall fly away.

ALFRED TENNYSON.

## WHAT ROBIN TOLD

How do robins build their nests?
Robin Redbreast told me—

First a wisp of yellow hay
  In a pretty round they lay;
Then some shreds of downy floss
  Feathers too, and bits of moss,
Woven with a sweet, sweet song,
  This way, that way, and across;
*That's* what robin told me
  That's what robin told me.

Where do robins hide their nests?
  Robin Redbreast told me—
Up among the leaves so deep,
  Where the sunbeams rarely creep,
Long before the winds are cold,
  Long before the leaves are gold,
Bright-eyed stars will peep and see
  Baby robins—one, two, three:
That's what robin told me,
  That's what robin told me.

GEO. COOPER.

## WRENS AND ROBINS [1]

Wrens and robins in the hedge,
Wrens and robins here and there;
Building, perching, fluttering
    Everywhere.

CHRISTINA ROSSETTI.

## A FAIRY IN ARMOR

He put his acorn helmet on;
It was plumed with the silk of the thistle down;
The corslet plate that guarded his breast
Was once the wild bee's golden vest;

[1] *From "Sing Song." By permission of the Macmillan Co.*

His cloak, of a thousand mingled dyes,
Was formed of wings of butterflies;
His shield was the shell of a lady-bug green,
Studs of gold on a ground of green;
And the quivering lance which he brandished bright,
Was the sting of a wasp he had slain in fight.
Swift he bestrode his fire-fly steed;
   He bared his blade of the bent-grass blue;
He drove his spurs of the cockle-seed,
   And away like a glance of thought he flew,
To skim the heavens, and follow far
The fiery trail of the rocket-star.

JOSEPH RODMAN DRAKE.

## A MIDNIGHT PERFORMANCE

If you could creep out on a summer's night
And tip-toe away to a wood,
Holding your breath and making yourself
As little as ever you could,

It wouldn't be long till you heard a sound
As small as a piece of thread
And then if you'd listen and not even wink
You could hear what the fairies said.

For on magical nights when the moon hangs low
And stars make a firework's display
It's all understood they will gather there
To put on a fairy play.

They make their own costumes of silver mist
And powder each tip of a wing
And then a green froggy in charge of the band
Tells all of the crickets to sing.

The glossiest glow-worms will carry their lamps
And form in a glimmer-y line,

Then the curtain of cobwebs will slowly arise
While they make the wee foot-lights shine.

Then fairies will twirl themselves out on the stage,
All flickering that way and this,
And leaves in the gallery will clap their hands
Till the actors have thrown them a kiss.

So down comes the curtain and "blink" go the lights
While moonbeams stay whiter than cream
Till you find yourself home in your own little bed
And pretend you've been dreaming a dream.

HELEN WING.

## DIFFERENCES

Daddy goes a-riding in a motor painted grey,
He makes a lot of snorty noise before he gets away;
The fairies go a-riding when they wish to take their ease,
The fairies go a-riding on the backs of bumblebees.

Daddy goes a-sailing in a jolly wooden boat,
He takes a lot of tackle and his very oldest coat;
The fairies go a-sailing, and I wonder they get home,
The fairies go a-sailing on a little scrap of foam.

Daddy goes a-climbing with a knapsack and a stick,
The rocks are very hard and steep, his boots are very thick;
But the fairies go a-climbing (I've seen them there in crowds),
The fairies go a-climbing on the mountains in the clouds.

ROSE FYLEMAN.

## FAIRIES' LIGHTS

Fireflies are fairies' lights—
Twink! Blinkety! Wink!

First the fairies turn them on
Then turn them off with a blink!

The fairies never dance by day,
For night is best—they think.
The fireflies turn on and off—
Twink! Blinkety! Wink!

ALICE WILKINS

## FAIRY AEROPLANES

The fairies, too, have aeroplanes,
To carry them about,
That swoop, and soar, and dart, and dip,
And circle in and out.

So when their little wings are tired,
They summon one of these,
And sail above the garden beds
Or anywhere they please.

The fairies' aeroplanes are safe
And never do capsize,
They're very beautiful and gay,
Because they're butterflies.

ANNE BLACKWELL PAYNE.

## FAIRY FRILLY

Fairy Frilly for half an hour
Went to sleep in a poppy flower—
Went to sleep in her little green frock,
And the time of the ball was ten o'clock.
Quarter to ten and five to ten
Ticked from the dandelion clock again,
But Fairy Frilly was deaf to all,
*And ten was the time of the fairy ball!*

Little West Wind came by that way,
And he pulled off the petal where Frilly lay,
Pulled it off with the fairy on it,
And blew with a great big breath upon it.
Off sailed the petal, Frilly and all—
And *that's* how she managed to get to the ball.

FLORENCE HOATSON.

## FAIRY FROLIC [1]

By a silver fountain,
  In a magic hour,
Once I saw a Fairy,
  Lovely as a flower;
Rainbow morning-glories
  Watched her from above;
Waterlilies peeped beneath,
  Just to show their love!

Fast as almond petals
  On a windy day,
Little white feet twinkled
  In her fairy play;
Little starry white hands,
  Frail as snowdrops small,
Tossed a colored bubble up
  For a fairy ball.

Never sheery butterfly
  Had such wondrous grace;
I could see her shimmering wings,
  See her rose-leaf face;
Never golden sunbeam
  Danced with such delight;
Never moonbeam shone so fair
  On a summer night.

[1] *Reprinted by permission of Frederick A. Stokes Co. from "Fairyland," by Grenbry Outhwaite and Annie R. Rentoul.*

O that fairy frolic!
   Not a step I stirred,
Only wished a tiny wish—
   But the Fairy heard.
Heard my heart go pit-a-pat,
   Though I never spoke;
Puff! the Fairy vanished,
   And the bubble broke.

ANNIE R. RENTOUL.

## FAIRY UMBRELLAS

Out in the waving meadow grass
   The pretty daisies grow,
I love to see their golden eyes,
   Their petals white as snow.

I wonder if the fairies use
   The dainty little flowers,
To keep their frocks from getting wet
   In sudden April showers.

LUCY DIAMOND.

## PIPES AND DRUMS

A little Pixie Piper went
   A-piping through the glens;
Some folks who heard him thought his notes
   A robin's or a wren's.

*"How late to hear a robin sing,*
   *It must be nearly ten!*
(The Pixie Piper chuckled and
   Went piping down the glen.)

*"It wasn't quite a robin's note,*
   *I fancy 'twas a wren."*

(The Pixie Piper chuckled and
Went piping down the glen.)

If we'd been there we might have made
The same mistakes ourselves;
The only folks who knew the truth
Were Goblins, Gnomes, and Elves.

The Pixies sought their pixie pipes—
The Goblins fetched their drums—
The Gnomes and Elves called everywhere,
"The Pixie Piper comes!"

He led them slowly through the town
And slowly back again—
Some folks who heard them thought the drums
Were raindrops on the pane,

And, as the Goblin band drew near,
Cried, "Listen to the hail!"
(The Goblin drummers chuckled and
Went drumming down the dale.)

Be careful, pray, the next wet day,
To make quite sure yourselves,
The patter's *really* raindrops—not
The drums of drumming Elves.

LILIAN HOLMES.

## RING-A-RING O' FAIRIES

Ring-A-Ring o' fairies,
Pixies, sprites and elves,
Dancing with a little boy
As nimble as themselves.
Charm a sleepy song-thrush
To sing a fairy tune;

Was ever such a pretty dance
Seen beneath the moon?

M. NIGHTINGALE.

## THE APPLE-ELF

The Apple-Elf lives up aloft
  In yonder apple tree.
I often think I see him peep
  Between the leaves at me.

He likes it when the wind is high,
  For then he sits and swings,
So high, so low, upon a branch
  The while he gaily sings.

Then shakes a lot of apples down,
  With many a laughing cry;
And I run out and pick them up
  To make an apple pie.

SHEILA E. BRAINE.

## THE BEST GAME THE FAIRIES PLAY

The best game the fairies play,
  The best game of all,
Is sliding down steeples—
  (You know they're very tall).
You fly to the weathercock,
  And when you hear it crow
You fold your wings and clutch your things
  And then let go!

They have a million other games—
  Cloud-catching's one,
And mud-mixing after rain
  Is heaps and heaps of fun;

But when you go and stay with them
Never mind the rest,
Take my advice—they're very nice,
But steeple-sliding's best!

ROSE FYLEMAN.

## THE ELF AND THE DORMOUSE

Under a toadstool crept a wee Elf,
Out of the rain, to shelter himself.

Under the toadstool sound asleep,
Sat a big Dormouse all in a heap.

Trembled the wee Elf, frightened, and yet
Fearing to fly away lest he get wet.

To the next shelter—maybe a mile!
Sudden the wee Elf smiled a wee smile,

Tugged till the toadstool toppled in two.
Holding it over him, gaily he flew.

Soon he was safe home, dry as could be.
Soon woke the Dormouse—"Good gracious me!

"Where is my toadstool?" loud he lamented.
—And that's how umbrellas first were invented.

OLIVER HERFORD.

## THE ENCHANTED GARDEN

Ding! Dong! The moon is gleaming;
Tiptoe through a faery glade
To a little garden dreaming
In a green and silver shade.

Hush! Hush! A wood-wind's creeping
 Past the place where poppies dwell,
Where the nightingale is sleeping
 In a bower of asphodel.

Where the King of Faery's daughter
 And an Elf with magic lute
Play beside the trembling water
 Of a fountain that is mute,

While in silver silence, flowers,
 Rose and gold and amethyst,
Sleep away the moonlit hours,
 Vanish in the morning mist.

Ding! Dong! The moon is gleaming;
 Tiptoe through a faery glade
To a little garden dreaming
 In a green and silver shade.

MARJORIE BARROWS.

## THE FAIRIES

Up the airy mountain,
 Down the rushy glen,
We daren't go a-hunting
 For the fear of little men;
Wee folk, good folk,
 Trooping all together;
Green jacket, red cap,
 And white owl's feather!

Down along the rocky shore
 Some make their home,
They live on crispy pancakes
 Of yellow tide-foam;

Some in the reeds
   Of the black mountain lake,
With frogs for their watch-dogs,
   All night awake.

. . . . .

Up the airy mountain,
   Down the rushy glen,
We daren't go a-hunting
   For fear of little men;
Wee folk, good folk,
   Trooping all together;
Green jacket, red cap,
   And white owl's feather!

WILLIAM ALLINGHAM.

## THE FAIRY FOLK

Come cuddle close in daddy's coat
   Beside the fire so bright,
And hear about the fairy folk
   That wander in the night.
For when the stars are shining clear
   And all the world is still,
They float across the silver moon
   From hill to cloudy hill.

Their caps of red, their cloaks of green,
   Are hung with silver bells,
And when they're shaken with the wind
   Their merry ringing swells.
And riding on the crimson moth,
   With black spots on her wings,
They guide them down the purple sky
   With golden bridle rings.

They love to visit girls and boys
   To see how sweet they sleep,

To stand beside their cosy cots
  And at their faces peep.
For in the whole of fairy land
  They have no finer sight
Than little children sleeping sound
  With faces rosy bright.

On tip-toe crowding round their heads,
  When bright the moonlight beams,
They whisper little tender words
  That fill their minds with dreams;
And when they see a sunny smile,
  With lightest finger tips
They lay a hundred kisses sweet
  Upon the ruddy lips.

And then the little spotted moths
  Spread out their crimson wings,
And bear away the fairy crowd
  With shaking bridle rings.
Come, bairnies, hide in daddy's coat,
  Beside the fire so bright—
Perhaps the little fairy folk
  Will visit you to-night.

ROBERT BIRD.

## THE FOUNTAIN

Upon the terrace where I play
A little fountain sings all day
    A tiny tune;
It leaps and prances in the air—
I saw a little fairy there
    This afternoon.

The jumping fountain never stops—
He sat upon the highest drops
    And bobbed about;

His legs were waving in the sun,
He seemed to think it splendid fun—
I heard him shout.

The sparrows watched him from a tree,
A robin bustled up to see
Along the path:
I thought my wishing-bone would break,
I wished so much that I could take
A fairy bath.

ROSE FYLEMAN.

## THE GARDEN PATH

If *you* go down the garden path,
All that you will see
Are daffodils and gilly-flowers,
Beneath the lilac tree;
And a clump of double daisies, and a red anemone.

If *you* go down the garden path,
All that you will hear
Is a blackbird in the hawthorne bush,
Piping loud and clear;
And green leaves rustling gently, and a wild bee humming near.

If *I* go down the garden path,
Softly, all alone,
Then I shall see a fairy peep
From every bud half-blown;
While every blossom sings a song to music of its own.

If *I* go down the garden path,
When the stars are lit,
I shall join the fairy ring
And merrily dance in it;
For all the fairies know me, and they aren't afraid a bit!

CHARLOTTE DRUIT COLE.

## THE LITTLE ELF

I met a little Elf-man, once,
Down where the lilies blow.
I asked him why he was so small,
And why he didn't grow.
He slightly frowned, and with his eye
He looked me through and through.
"I'm quite as big for me," said he,
"As you are big for you."

JOHN KENDRICK BANGS.

## THE SNOW

The snow's a snuggly blanket
The fairies tuck around
The sleeping posies in their beds,
Safe in the crumbly ground.

They cover all so gently
And softly say, "Good night,"
Then steal away and leave them,
All snug and warm and white.

NELLIE BURGET MILLER.

There was a little goblin
Who played a little tune,
He played it in the morning
And in the afternoon;
He played it rather loudly,
He played it with delight,
He held his head up proudly,
And tucked his lips in tight.

AGNES GROZIER HERBERTSON.

## BABY CORN

A happy mother stalk of corn
  Held close a baby ear,
And whispered: "Cuddle up to me,
  I'll keep you warm, my dear.
I'll give you petticoats of green
  With many a tuck and fold
To let out daily as you grow;
  For you will soon be old."

A funny little baby that,
  For though it had no eye,
It had a hundred mouths; 'twas well
  It did not want to cry.
The mother put in each small mouth
  A hollow thread of silk,
Through which the sun and rain and air
  Provided babies milk.

The petticoats were gathered close
  Where all the threadlets hung.
And still as summer days went on
  To mother-stalk it clung;
And all the time it grew and grew—
  Each kernel drank the milk
By day, by night, in shade, in sun,
  From its own thread of silk.

And each grew strong and full and round
  And each was shining white;
The gores and seams were all let out,
  The green skirts fitted tight.
The ear stood straight and large and tall,
  And when it saw the sun,
Held up its emerald satin gown
  To say: "Your work is done."

"You're large enough," said Mother Stalk,
"And now there's no more room
For you to grow." She tied the threads
Into a soft brown plume—
It floated out upon the breeze
To greet the dewy morn.
And then the baby said: "Now I'm
A full-grown ear of corn!"

UNKNOWN.

## DEEP IN THE WOODS

I know a place
Where sunbeams dancing in and out
With violets play peek-a-boo;
Where brooks meandering about
Are mirrors for the heaven's blue;
Where the gnarled and twisted grape-vine swing
Weighs down the boughs from which it twines;
Where the nests that house young feathered things
Are safe among the leaves and vines;
Where the spider with a silken thread
Weaves a bridge from bush to bush across;
Where the cricket chirps from a grassy bed
And the ground is carpeted with moss
Deep in the woods!

MILDRED D. SHACKLETT.

## FARM LIFE

I love to go to see Aunt Flo
And chase her old fat hen
That wobbles all around the yard
Again and then again!

I love to watch the piggies eat
And hear the horses neigh

And run the little calves a race
And slide down stacks of hay.

And when I'm dusted up a lot
And sort of skinned my knees,
I like to go inside and rest,
And have some cottage cheese.

RUTH EDNA STANTON.

## MR. FINNEY'S TURNIP

Mr. Finney had a turnip
  And it grew behind the barn;
And it grew and it grew,
  And that turnip did no harm.

There it grew and it grew
  Till it could grow no longer;
Then his daughter Lizzie picked it up
  And put it in the cellar.

There it lay and it lay
  Till it began to rot;
And his daughter Susie took it
  And put it in the pot.

And they boiled it and boiled it
  As long as they were able;
And then his daughters took it
  And put it on the table.

Mr. Finney and his wife
  They sat them down to sup;
And they ate and they ate
  And they ate that turnip up.

UNKNOWN.

## THE HAYLOFT

Through all the pleasant meadow-side
  The grass grew shoulder-high,
Till the shining scythes went far and wide
  And cut it down to dry.

These green and sweetly smelling crops
  They led in wagons home;
And they piled them here in mountain tops
  For mountaineers to roam.

Here is Mount Clear, Mount Rusty-Nail,
  Mount Eagle and Mount High;—
The mice that in these mountains dwell,
  No happier are than I!

O what a joy to clamber there,
  O what a place for play,
With the sweet, the dim, the dusty air,
  The happy hills of hay!

ROBERT LOUIS STEVENSON.

## THE ESCAPE

I'm not afraid of rats and mice
  (At least not much),
A spider I can look at twice
  (And even touch);
I do not mind the cows and sheep
That people in the country keep
(No matter how they turn and stare
I pass along and never care);
But once when I was out a-walking
A great gray goose came at me squawking;

He flew nip-nipping at my knee,
I was as scared as I could be
I shouldn't have escaped at all
Without my little parasol!

EMILY ROSE BURT.

## THE PROUD VEGETABLES

In a funny little garden not much bigger than a mat,
There lived a thriving family, its members all were fat;
But some were short, and some were tall, and some were almost round,
And some ran high on bamboo poles, and some lay on the ground.

Of these old Father Pumpkin was, perhaps, the proudest one.
He claimed to trace his family vine directly from the sun.
"We both are round and yellow, we both are bright," said he,
"A stronger family likeness one could scarcely wish to see."

Old Mrs. Squash hung on the fence; she had a crooked neck,
Perhaps 'twas hanging made it so,—her nerves were quite a wreck,
Near by, upon a planted row of fagots, dry and lean,
The young cucumbers climbed to swing their Indian clubs of green.

MARY MCNEIL FENOLLOSA.

## VEGETABLES

A carrot has a green fringed top;
  A beet is royal red;
And lettuces are curious
  All curled and run to head.

Some beans have strings to tie them on,
And, what is still more queer,
Ripe corn is nothing more or less
Than one enormous ear!

But when potatoes all have eyes,
Why is it they should be
Put in the ground and covered up—
Where it's too dark to see?

RACHEL LYMAN FIELD.

## WINDMILL

The windmill stands up like a flower on the hill
With its petals a-whirling, they seldom stay still,
And its funny old voice creaking all the long day
As it scolds little breezes for running away.

JOHN FARRAR.

## A LOVELY BED

Each morning bees and butterflies
Have wiped the dewdrops from their eyes
And flown away on whirring wings
Before our bell for breakfast rings!
They sleep in hollyhocks so pink—
A soft and lovely bed I think!

MATTIE LEE HAUSGEN.

## A YELLOW PANSY

To the wall of the old green garden
A butterfly quivering came;
His wings on the sombre lichens
Played like a yellow flame.

He looked at the gay geraniums
And sleepy four-o'clocks;
He looked at the low lanes bordered
With the glossy-growing box.

He longed for the peace and the silence,
And the shadows that lengthened there,
And his wee wild heart was weary
Of skimming the endless air.

And now in the old green garden
I know not how it came—
A single pansy is blooming,
Bright as a yellow flame.

And whenever a gay gust passes,
It quivers as if in pain,
For the butterfly-soul that is in it
Longs for the winds again!

HELEN GRAY CONE.

## ALONE

White daisies are down in the meadows,
And queer little beetles and things,
And sometimes nice rabbits and field mice,
And blackbirds with red on their wings.

I want to explore all alone,
With nobody spying around,
All alone! All alone, all alone!
It has such a wonderful sound.

Just I on the dusty town road,
With my bank money safe in my purse.
Do you think I shall ever grow up?
Or shall I just always have nurse?

JOHN FARRAR.

## APPLE BLOSSOM

"Lady Apple Blossom
Just arrived in town,
Wears a light green bonnet
And a snowy gown.

The pretty dress is—
What do you think?
Five white petals
Just touched with pink."

KATE L. BROWN.

## APPLE BLOSSOMS

The apple blossoms grow so high
Upon the branches of our tree,
I can't reach up to smell them; so
They send their perfume down to me.

HELEN WING.

## APPLE BLOSSOMS

There is a day
That comes in spring
When apple trees
Are blossoming.
They blossom out
So quick some morn
It's like a giant
Popping corn.

And from my window
I can smell
The apple blossoms
Very well.

And leaning from
   My window-cliff
I sniff and sniff
   And sniff and sniff.

And just as quick
   They drop away.
I wish the apple
   Trees would stay
In bloom at least
   A week or two;
But that is not
   The way they do.

Almost at once
   The petals fall
Down on the grass
   And garden wall.
They go adrift
   On every breeze
Like snowflakes off
   The apple trees.

It is the oddest
   Thing to see:
The lawn as green
   As green can be,
And then the orchard
   Where each row
Of apple trees
   Stands in the snow.

RALPH BERGENGREN.

## CROCUS

Dainty little cups of color,
   Purple, white and gold,
Lifting up your smiling faces
   To the sky so cold;

Springing upward from the grasses,
  Calling out with cheer:
"Spring has come! forget the winter!
  Crocuses are here!"

MARION MITCHELL WALKER.

## CROCUS

Warm sunshine came down
  On a sweet April day,
To work in a garden,
  And have a fine play,
With the plants that all winter
  Had slept there.

He came to a little
  Brown bulb at one side,
And said to himself,
  "Under this will I hide
For I see a black cloud
  In the sky."

So he tucked himself down
  In the soft yielding earth,
While the little brown bulb
  Was shaking with mirth;
"For sunshine," said she,
  "Makes me grow."

Then down came the rain;
  And the bulb that no more
A little brown bulb was to be,
  Just opened her eyes;
And what do you think?—
  Why, a bright yellow crocus
    Was she!

UNKNOWN.

## DANDELION[1]

O little soldier with the golden helmet,
What are you guarding on my lawn?
You with your green gun
And your yellow beard,
Why do you stand so stiff?
There is only the grass to fight!

HILDA CONKLING.

## DANDELION

There's a dandy little fellow,
Who dresses all in yellow,
In yellow with an overcoat of green;
With his hair all crisp and curly,
In the springtime bright and early
A-tripping o'er the meadow he is seen.
Through all the bright June weather,
Like a jolly little tramp,
He wanders o'er the hillside, down the road;
Around his yellow feather,
The gypsy fireflies camp;
His companions are the woodlark and the toad.

But at last this little fellow
Doffs his dainty coat of yellow,
And very feebly totters o'er the green;
For he very old is growing
And with hair all white and flowing,
A-nodding in the sunlight he is seen.
Oh, poor dandy, once so spandy,
Golden dancer on the lea!

[1] *Reprinted by permission from "Poems by a Little Girl." Copyright, 1920, by Frederick A. Stokes Co.*

Older growing, white hair flowing,
Poor little baldhead dandy now is he!

NELLIE M. GARABRANT.

## DANDELION

There was a pretty dandelion
With lovely, fluffy hair,
That glistened in the sunshine
And in the summer air.
But oh! this pretty dandelion
Soon grew old and grey;
And, sad to tell! her charming hair
Blew many miles away.

UNKNOWN.

## DANDELIONS

Upon a showery night and still,
Without a sound of warning,
A trooper band surprised the hill,
And held it in the morning.
We were not waked by bugle notes,
No cheer our dreams invaded,
And yet, at dawn their yellow coats
On the green slopes paraded.

We careless folk the deed forgot;
'Till one day, idly walking,
We marked upon the self-same spot
A crowd of vet'rans talking.
They shook their trembling heads and gray
With pride and noiseless laughter;
When, well-a-day! they blew away,
And ne'er were heard of after!

HELEN GRAY CONE.

## DANDY DANDELION

When Dandy Dandelion wakes
And combs his yellow hair,
The ant his cup of dewdrop takes
And sets his bed to air;
The worm hides in a quilt of dirt
To keep the thrush away,
The beetle dons his pansy shirt—
They know that it is day.

The caterpillars haste to milk
The cowslips in the grass;
The spider in his web of silk,
Looks out for flies that pass.
These humble people leap from bed
They know the night is done:
When Dandy spreads his golden head
They think he is the Sun!

Dear Dandy truly does not smell
As sweet as some bouquets;
No florist gathers him to sell,
He withers in a vase;
Yet in the grass he's emperor,
And lord of high renown;
And grateful little folk adore
His bright and shining crown.

CHRISTOPHER MORLEY.

## FOOLISH FLOWERS

We've Foxgloves in our garden;
How careless they must be
To leave their gloves out hanging
Where everyone can see!

And Bachelors leave their Buttons
  In the same careless way,
If I should do the same with mine,
  What would my mother say?

We've lots of Larkspurs in the Yard—
  Larks only fly and sing—
Birds surely don't need spurs because
  They don't ride anything!

And as for Johnny-Jump-Ups—
  I saw a hornet light
On one of them the other day,
  He didn't jump a mite!

RUPERT SARGENT HOLLAND.

## GOLDEN TACKS

Miss April's come and I have found
She's spread a carpet on the ground.
It's the nicest rug I've ever seen,
So big and soft and bright and green.
It hides the Earth's old dirty brown
And all the ugly-wrinkly cracks—
It can't blow off, it's fastened down
With golden dandelion tacks!

MILDRED D. SHACKLETT.

## GROWING IN THE VALE

Growing in the vale,
  By the uplands hilly,
Growing straight and frail,
  Lady Daffydowndilly.

In a golden crown,
And a scant green gown
  While the spring blows chilly,

Lady Daffydown,
Sweet Daffydowndilly.

CHRISTINA ROSSETTI.

## LILIES OF THE VALLEY

Down in the grassy lowland dells,
They softly swing—white lily bells;
A pale green stem upon which grows
Fair white-frilled cups in tiny rows.
Each wee flower has a heart of gold,
Each cup a drop of dew would hold;
And by their fragrance you may know
Where lilies of the valley grow.

MARION MITCHELL WALKER.

## MY BARROW

I've got a barrow; it's very small,
It isn't a useful one at all.
Its sides are green, and its wheel is red,
I wish it had *no* paint on instead;
No paint on it but bare brown wood
To show it works as a barrow should,
Carrying rubbish and stones away
From people's flower-beds every day;
And not a toy that hides itself
Under the lowest nursery shelf!

ELIZABETH FLEMING.

## PUSSY WILLOWS

I came on them yesterday (merely by chance),
Those newly born pussies, asleep on a branch;
Each curled up so tight in a fluff of a ball
That I could not see ear-points or tail-tips at all;

But I thought that I heard, when the March wind was stirring,
A soft little sound like the note of purring.
I wonder if they would have leaped from their bough
And arched their wee backs with a frightened "Meow!"
If I dared to tell them in one warning cry
That a fierce patch of dogwood was growing close by.

ROWENA BASTIN BENNETT.

## PUSSY WILLOWS

There are willow pussies
  Clad in furry hoods,
And a robin singing
  In the maple woods.
There's a springing crocus,
  And a budding larch,
Who'd ever think that Springtime
  Came along in March.

UNKNOWN.

## QUEEN ANNE'S LACE

Queen Anne, Queen Anne, has washed her lace
  (She chose a summer's day)
And hung it in a grassy place
  To whiten, if it may.

Queen Anne, Queen Anne, has left it there,
  And slept the dewy night;
Then waked, to find the sunshine fair,
  And all the meadows white.

Queen Anne, Queen Anne, is dead and gone
  (She died a summer's day),
But left her lace to whiten on
  Each weed-entangled way!

MARY LESLIE NEWTON.

## THE NASTURTIUMS

"I am the gay Nasturtium.
I bloom in gardens fine.
Among the garden flowers
My slender stalk I twine.
Bright orange is my color—
The eyes of all to please—
I have a tube of honey
For all the honey bees."

UNKNOWN.

## THE SLEEPY TULIPS

Each evening tulips close their eyes
When the dew begins to fall;
I wonder if they really sleep,
They stand so straight and tall!

I couldn't sleep if I stood up,—
A soft white bed holds me:
But all the day I run and play,
While tulips rest you see!

MARION MITCHELL WALKER.

## WATER LILY

I'd like to be a water-lily sleeping on the river,
Where solemn rushes whisper, and funny ripples quiver,
All day I'd watch the blue sky—all night I'd watch the black,
Floating in the soft waves, dreaming on my back.

And when I'd tire of dreaming, I'd call a passing fish,
"I want to find the sea!" I'd shout, "Come! you can grant my wish!"

He'd bite me from my moorings, and softly I would slip
To the center of the river, like an ocean-going ship.

The waves would lash upon me. The wind would blow me
fast,
And, oh, what shores and wonders would greet me as I passed!
Yes, if I were a water-lily, I'd sail to sea in state—
A green frog for my captain, and a dragon fly for mate!

JOHN FARRAR.

## WHEN WE WENT GATHERING CAT-TAILS

When we went gathering cat-tails—
Roger and Tip and I—
Came gliding down the still blue air
A spangled butterfly.
Like burnished sails its wings were spread,
That tiny craft to steer,
And it moved to some secret thread of song
That only it could hear.

RACHEL LYMAN FIELD.

## WISHING

Ring-ting! I wish I were a Primrose,
A bright yellow Primrose, blowing in the Spring!
The stooping bough above me,
The wandering bee to love me,
The fern and moss to creep across,
And the Elm-tree for King!

Nay,—stay! I wish I were an Elm-tree,
A great lofty Elm-tree, with green leaves gay!
The winds would set them dancing,
The sun and moonshine glance in,
The Birds would house among the boughs,
And sweetly sing!

O-no! I wish I were a Robin,
A Robin or a little Wren, everywhere to go;
Through forest, field, or garden,
And ask no leave or pardon,
Till Winter comes with icy thumbs
To ruffle up our wing.

Well-tell! Where should I fly to,
Where go to sleep in the dark wood or dell?
Before a day was over,
Home comes the rover,
For Mother's kiss,—sweeter this
Than any other thing.

WM. ALLINGHAM.

## A CHRISTMAS FOLK-SONG

The little Jesus came to town;
The wind blew up, the wind blew down;
Out in the street the wind was bold;
Now who could house Him from the cold?

Then opened wide a stable door,
Fair were the rushes on the floor;
The Ox put forth a horned head:
"Come, little Lord, here make Thy bed."

Up rose the Sheep were folded near:
"Thou Lamb of God, come, enter here."
He entered there to rush and reed,
Who was the Lamb of God indeed.

The little Jesus came to town;
With ox and sheep He laid Him down;
Peace to the byre, peace to the fold,
For that they housed Him from the cold!

LIZETTE WOODWORTH REESE.

## A VALENTINE

Frost flowers on the window glass,
Hopping chickadees that pass,
Bare old elms that bend and sway,
Pussywillows soft and gray,

Silver clouds across the sky,
Lacy snowflakes flitting by,
Icicles like fringe in line—
That is Outdoor's valentine!

ELEANOR HAMMOND.

## A VISIT FROM ST. NICHOLAS

'Twas the night before Christmas, when all through the house
Not a creature was stirring, not even a mouse;
The stockings were hung by the chimney with care,
In hopes that St. Nicholas soon would be there.
The children were nestled all snug in their beds,
While visions of sugar-plums danced in their heads;
And mamma in her 'kerchief, and I in my cap,
Had just settled our brains for a long winter's nap,
When out on the lawn there arose such a clatter,
I sprang from my bed to see what was the matter.
Away to the window I flew like a flash,
Tore open the shutters and threw up the sash.
The moon on the breast of the new-fallen snow
Gave the lustre of mid-day to objects below,
When, what to my wondering eyes should appear,
But a miniature sleigh, and eight tiny reindeer,
With a little old driver, so lively and quick,
I knew in a moment it must be St. Nick.
More rapid than eagles his coursers they came,
And he whistled and shouted, and called them by name;

"Now, Dasher! now, Dancer! now, Prancer and Vixen!
On, Comet! on, Cupid! on, Donder and Blitzen!
To the top of the porch! to the top of the wall!
Now dash away! dash away! dash away all!"
As dry leaves that before the wild hurricane fly,
When they meet with an obstacle, mount to the sky,
So up to the house-top the coursers they flew,
With a sleigh full of toys, and St. Nicholas too.
And then in a twinkling, I heard on the roof
The prancing and pawing of each little hoof.
As I drew in my head, and was turning around,
Down the chimney St. Nicholas came with a bound.
He was dressed all in fur, from his head to his foot,
And his clothes were all covered with ashes and soot;
A bundle of toys he had flung on his back,
And he looked like a peddler just opening his pack.
His eyes—how they twinkled! his dimples how merry!
His cheeks were like roses, his nose like a cherry!
His droll little mouth was drawn up like a bow,
And the beard on his chin was as white as the snow;
The stump of a pipe he held tight in his teeth,
And the smoke it encircled his head like a wreath;
He was chubby and plump, a right jolly old elf,
And I laughed when I saw him, in spite of myself;
A wink of his eye and a twist of his head,
Soon gave me to know I had nothing to dread;
He spoke not a word, but went straight to his work,
And filled all the stockings; then turned with a jerk,
And laying his finger aside of his nose
And giving a nod, up the chimney he rose;
He sprang to his sleigh, to his team gave a whistle,
And away they all flew like the down of a thistle.
But I heard him exclaim, ere he drove out of sight,
"Happy Christmas to all, and to all a good-night."

CLEMENT C. MOORE.

## AMBITION

Don't you think the trees remember
What day happens in December:
Hardly rustling, lest they should
Fail at being green and good;
Asking other shrubs that wait,
"Tell me, are my needles straight?"
Each one hoping, Oh, to be
Chosen for a Christmas Tree.

ANNE BLACKWELL PAYNE.

## AMERICA

My country! 'tis of thee,
Sweet land of liberty,
Of thee I sing;
Land where my fathers died,
Land of the Pilgrim's pride!
From ev'ry mountain side
Let freedom ring.

My native country, thee,
Land of the noble free,
Thy name I love;
I love thy rocks and rills,
Thy woods and templed hills;
My heart with rapture thrills
Like that above.

Let music swell the breeze,
And ring from all the trees
Sweet freedom's song;
Let mortal tongues awake,
Let all that breathe partake,
Let rocks their silence break,
The sound prolong.

Our fathers' God! to Thee,
Author of liberty,
To Thee we sing;
Long may our land be bright
With freedom's holy light!
Protect us by Thy might,
Great God, our King!

S. F. SMITH.

## AN EASTER SURPRISE

I play my garden is a church—
No roof or steeple on it—
And flowers that grow row after row
All wear an Easter bonnet.
But oh, I was surprised today
To see they liked my sprinkler spray!

LEONA COVEY.

## APRIL FOOL

Small April sobbed,
"I'm going to cry!
Please give me a cloud
To wipe my eye!"

Then, "April fool!"
She laughed instead
And smiled a rainbow
Overhead!

ELEANOR HAMMOND.

## AT CHRISTMAS TIME

When Santa Claus has trimmed our Christmas tree,
It twinkles with a lot of tiny lights,

And tinsel makes its boughs shine prettily,
  The way the frost shines on cold moonlight nights.

And every evening in vacation time
  We light the stars of green and gold and red,
And sing together some sweet Christmas rime
  Before we say our prayers and go to bed.

MARY BRENNAN CLAPP.

## BUNDLES

A bundle is a funny thing,
It always sets me wondering;
For whether it is thin or wide,
You never know just what's inside.
Especially on Christmas week,
Temptation is so great to peek;
Now wouldn't it be much more fun
If shoppers carried things undone?

JOHN FARRAR.

## SONG

Why do bells for Christmas ring?
Why do little children sing?

Once a lovely, shining star,
Seen by shepherds from afar,
Gently moved until its light
Made a manger's cradle bright.
There a darling baby lay,
Pillowed soft upon the hay;
And its mother sang and smiled,
"This is Christ, the holy child!"

Therefore bells for Christmas ring,
Therefore little children sing.

EUGENE FIELD.

## OUR FLAG

There are many flags in many lands,
There are flags of every hue;
But there is no flag, however grand,
Like our own Red, White, and Blue.

MARY HOWLISTON.

## CHRISTMAS EVE

"Tick-tock," said the Nursery Clock,
"Please remember that little sock:
Nannie, mend the hole in the toe;
The goodies will tumble out, you know.
Tick-tock, tick-tock,"
Said the clickity-clackity Nursery Clock.

"Hush, hush," said Santa Claus,
As he peeped inside the bedroom doors;
"I am looking around for a little sock,
Do you know where it is, please, Mr. Clock?"
"Tick-tock, tick-tock,
It hangs over there," said the Nursery Clock.

"Tick-tock," said the Nursery Clock,
And pointed straight at the little sock,
Oh, yes he did, for don't you see,
A clock has hands like you and me.
"Tick-tock, tick-tock;
I am always right," said the Nursery Clock.

FLORENCE HOATSON.

## CRADLE HYMN

Away in a manger, no crib for a bed,
The little Lord Jesus laid down His sweet head.
The stars in the bright sky looked down where He lay—
The little Lord Jesus asleep on the hay.

The cattle are lowing, the Baby awakes,
But little Lord Jesus, no crying He makes.
I love thee, Lord Jesus! look down from the sky,
And stay by my cradle till morning is nigh.

MARTIN LUTHER.

## EASTER EGGS

Humpty Dumpty has country cousins
Who come to the city in Spring by dozens;
They make such a brilliant show in town
You'd think that a rainbow had tumbled down.
Blue and yellow and pink and green,
The gayest gowns that ever were seen.
Purple and gold and oh! such style;
They are all the rage for a little while
But their visit is short for no one stays
After the Easter holidays.

UNKNOWN.

## HALLOWE'EN

Hallowe'en's the time for nuts
  And for apples, too,
And for funny faces that
  Stare and glare at you.
Right behind them is a friend,
  Jack or Bob or Bess.

Isn't it the greatest fun
  When you try to guess?

ANNA MEDARY.

## HALLOWE'EN

We had a Goblin party on the night of Hallowe'en
And all the children on our street were there.
And it was dark inside our house with only candlelight
And Jack-o'-lanterns standing by the stair.

There was a big enormous ghost that walked around the room
(The ghost was really Father in a sheet)
And he made moans and shook his head, but no one was afraid!
Because he gave them lollipops to eat.

I dressed up like a goblin in a last-year's Brownie suit;
(I made myself a tail that I could wag);
And Mary Ann rode on a broom and was a kind of witch
Who kept her magic secrets in a bag.

We bobbed for apples in a tub and caught them in our teeth
But I got water in my nose and eyes,
So I was glad when Mother called us to the dining room
For that was where we found the big surprise.

The table was more fancy than I'd ever seen before;
I couldn't tell what thing I liked the most,
The doughnuts or the pumpkin pie, the cider or ice cream,
All served to us by Mother and the Ghost.

When there was nothing left but crumbs, the children had to go,
'Cause it was past their time to go to bed;
Then everybody thanked us for the party, and they wished
That Hallowe'en came *every* week, they said.

HELEN WING.

## IF YOU'VE NEVER

If you've never seen an old witch
Riding through the sky—
Or never felt big bat's wings
Flopping, as they fly—
If you've never touched a white thing
Gliding through the air,
And knew it was a ghost because
You got a dreadful scare—
If you've never heard the night owls,
Crying, "Whoo-whoo-whoo?"
And never jumped at pumpkin eyes
Gleaming out at you—
If all of these exciting things
You've never heard nor seen,
Why then—you've missed a lot of fun,
Because—that's *Hallowe'en!*

ELSIE M. FOWLER.

## LONG, LONG AGO

Winds through the olive trees
  Softly did blow,
Round little Bethlehem
  Long, long ago.

Sheep on the hillside lay
  Whiter than snow;
Shepherds were watching them,
  Long, long ago.

Then from the happy sky,
  Angels bent low,
Singing their songs of joy,
  Long, long ago.

For in a manger bed,
  Cradled we know,
Christ came to Bethlehem,
  Long, long ago.

ANONYMOUS.

## MEETING THE EASTER BUNNY

On Easter morn at early dawn
  before the cocks were crowing,
I met a bob-tail bunnykin
  and asked where he was going,
" 'Tis in the house and out the house
  a-tipsy, tipsy-toeing,
'Tis round the house and 'bout the house
  a-lightly I am going."
"But what is that of every hue
  you carry in your basket?"
" 'Tis eggs of gold and eggs of blue;
  I wonder that you ask it.
" 'Tis chocolate eggs and bonbon eggs
  and eggs of red and gray,
For every child in every house
  on bonny Easter Day."
He perked his ears and winked his eye
  and twitched his little nose,
He shook his tail—what tail he had—
  and stood up on his toes.
"I must be gone before the sun;
  the east is growing gray;
'Tis almost time for bells to chime."—
  So he hippity-hopped away.

ROWENA BASTIN BENNETT.

"My dolly hung her stocking up,
  And Santa filled it full,
There were some nuts and sugar plums
  And a pretty dress of wool—

The sweetest lace-trimmed handkerchief
  And a painted china set—
Did your dolly hang her stocking up?
  What did your dolly get?"

UNKNOWN.

## MY FAVORITE TREE

Of all the many trees there are,
I love one best of all;
On top it has a silver star
Or a bright and shining ball.
It wears a gold and silver wig
Of lovely glittering hair,
And golden lights on every twig,
Like flowers, blossom there.
And apples red and walnuts brown
And a hundred things hang down,
The gayest sight you've ever seen—
Now can you guess what tree I mean?

MARGARET MUNSTERBERG.

## SANTA CLAUS

Old Santa Claus puts on his cap
  And buckles it under his chin.
He laughs and sings as he fills his sack
  And straps it over his sturdy back.
"I'll crowd all I can within,
  For girls and boys, such pretty toys—
I've dolls and drums and sugar-plums
  For all little girls and boys."

Old Santa Claus has reindeer brown
  And a sleigh with silver bells.
He rides over all the roofs in town
  And stops at the chimney and rattles down

And this pleasant story tells:—
"Christmas is here, with gladsome cheer,
And here are toys for girls and boys—
I've dolls and drums and sugar plums,
For all little girls and boys."

UNKNOWN.

## SANTA CLAUS AND THE MOUSE

One Christmas, when Santa Claus
Came to a certain house,
To fill the children's stockings there,
He found a little mouse.

"A Merry Christmas, little friend,"
Said Santa good and kind.
"The same to you, sir," said the mouse,
"I thought you wouldn't mind,

If I should stay awake tonight
And watch you for a while."
"You're very welcome, little mouse,"
Said Santa, with a smile.

And then he filled the stockings up
Before the mouse could wink—
From toe to top, from top to toe,
There wasn't left a chink.

"Now they won't hold another thing,"
Said Santa Claus with pride.
A twinkle came in mouse's eyes,
But humbly he replied:

"It's not polite to contradict—
Your pardon I implore—
But in the fullest stocking there
I could put one thing more."

"Oh, ho!" laughed Santa, "silly mouse,
Don't I know how to pack?
By filling stockings all these years
I should have learned the knack."

And then he took the stocking down
From where it hung so high,
And said, "Now put in one thing more
I give you leave to try."

The mousie chuckled to himself,
And then he softly stole
Right to the stocking's crowded toe
And gnawed a little hole!

"Now, if you please, good Santa Claus,
I've put in one thing more,
For you will own that little hole
Was not in there before."

How Santa Claus did laugh and laugh!
And then he gaily spoke,
"Well! you shall have a Christmas cheese
For that nice little joke."

If you don't think this story true,
Why! I can show to you
The very stocking with the hole
The little mouse gnawed through.

E. POULSSON.

## SMILING

I met a Jack-o'-Lantern, Hallowe'en,
With the saddest face that I have ever seen!
For his mouth was turning down,
Both his eyes were made to frown,
And his forehead wrinkled crossly in between.

I thought it such a pity that his style
Had to keep him so unhappy all the while,
For, as everybody knows,
Just the nicest thing that grows
Anywhere, on anybody, is a smile.

DIXIE WILLSON.

## ST. PATRICK'S DAY

Out by the front walk—have you seen?
Daffodilly is wearing a cap of green!
I wonder if she heard us say
Tomorrow is St. Patrick's Day!

ELEANOR HAMMOND.

## THANKSGIVING

The turkey is my favorite bird,
And mince my favorite pie,
And cranberry my favorite sauce—
  I wonder why?
I'm thankful for them all—aren't you?
And for the stuffing too!

MARGARET MUNSTERBERG.

## THANKSGIVING DAY

Over the river and through the wood,
  To grandfather's house we go;
    The horse knows the way
    To carry the sleigh
  Through the white and drifted snow.

Over the river and through the wood—
  Oh, how the wind does blow!

It stings the toes
And bites the nose,
As over the ground we go.

Over the river and through the wood,
To have a first-rate play.
Hear the bells ring,
"Ting-a-ling-ling!"
Hurrah for Thanksgiving Day!

Over the river and through the wood,
Trot fast my dapple-gray!
Spring over the ground,
Like a hunting-hound!
For this is Thanksgiving Day.

Over the river and through the wood,
And straight through the barnyard gate,
We seem to go
Extremely slow,
It is so hard to wait!

Over the river and through the wood—
Now grandmother's cap I spy!
Hurrah for the fun!
Is the pudding done?
Hurrah for the pumpkin-pie!

LYDIA MARIA CHILD.

## THE MAGIC VINE

A fairy seed I planted,
So dry and white and old;
There sprang a vine enchanted
With magic flowers of gold.

I watched it, I tended it,
   And truly, by and by
It bore a Jack o' lantern
   And a great Thanksgiving pie.

UNKNOWN.

## THE PILGRIMS CAME[1]

The Pilgrims came across the sea,
And never thought of you and me;
And yet it's strange the way
We think of them Thanksgiving Day.

We tell their story old and true
Of how they sailed across the blue,
And found a new land to be free
And built their homes quite near the sea.

Every child knows well the tale
Of how they bravely turned the sail,
And journeyed many a day and night
To worship God as they thought right.

The people think that they were sad,
And grave; I'm sure that they were glad—
They made Thanksgiving Day—that's fun—
We thank the Pilgrims every one!

ANNETTE WYNNE.

There's a big fat turkey on Grandfather's farm
   Who thinks he's very gay.
He spreads his tail into a great big fan
   And struts around all day.

[1] *Reprinted by permission from "For Days and Days: A Year-round Treasury of Verse for Children." Copyright, 1919, by Frederick A. Stokes Co.*

You should hear him gobble at the girls and boys
He thinks he's singing when he makes that noise.
He'll sing his song a different way,
Upon Thanksgiving Day.

UNKNOWN.

## THE EASTER AIRPLANE

A bumblebee went flying
In his very own machine,
'Twas the one he used for common
And everyone has seen.

He said, "This is Easter morning
I am thankful, it is true,
That I do not have the troubles
Other aviators do.

My motor's sure and faithful,
I can travel as I please,
And I don't have any accidents,
Or bad catastrophes."

Then, as he kept on sailing,
He remarked from up on high,
"That's the only kind of airplane
For anyone to buy."

CAROLYN R. FREEMAN.

## THE VALENTINE'S MESSAGE

Oh! gay pretty valentines gladly we send
That they may give pleasure to some little friend
Each valentine carries its message so true:
"A playmate or friend has been thinking of you."

MILDRED J. HILL.

## WHEN YOU SEND A VALENTINE

When you send a valentine—
That's the time for fun!
Push it underneath the door,
Ring the bell and run, run, run!
Ring the bell and run!

MILDRED J. HILL.

## A FIRE[1]

Why does a fire eat big sticks of wood?
I shouldn't like that for my food.
But the flames all lick their lips—it must taste good!

RACHEL LYMAN FIELD.

## A POP CORN SONG

Sing a song of pop-corn
When the snow-storms rage;
Fifty little brown men
Put into a cage.
Shake them till they laugh and leap
Crowding to the top;
Watch them burst their little coats
Pop!! Pop!! Pop!!

Sing a song of pop-corn
In the fire-light;
Fifty little fairies
Robed in fleecy white.
Through the shining wires see
How they skip and prance

[1] *From "Pointed People." By permission of the Macmillan Co.*

To the music of the flames;
Dance!! Dance!! Dance!!

Sing a song of pop-corn
Done the frolicking;
Fifty little fairies
Strung upon a string.
Cool and happy, hand in hand,
Sugar-spangled, fair;
Isn't that a necklace fit
For any child to wear?

NANCY BYRD TURNER.

## ANIMAL CRACKERS

Animal crackers and cocoa to drink,
That is the finest of suppers, I think;
When I'm grown up and can have what I please
I think I shall always insist upon these.

What do *you* choose when you're offered a treat?
When Mother says, "What would you like best to eat?"
Is it waffles and syrup, or cinnamon toast?
It's cocoa and animals that *I* love the most!

The kitchen's the cosiest place that I know:
The kettle is singing, the stove is aglow,
And there in the twilight, how jolly to see
The cocoa and animals waiting for me.

Daddy and Mother dine later in state,
With Mary to cook for them, Susan to wait;
But they don't have nearly as much fun as I
Who eat in the kitchen with Nurse standing by;
And Daddy once said he would like to be me
Having cocoa and animals once more for tea!

CHRISTOPHER MORLEY.

## BEDTIME

All day in Mother's garden here
I play and play and play.
But when night brings a dozen stars
I can no longer stay.

Sometimes the sun has hardly set
Before the stars begin.
A dozen stars come out so fast
And then I must go in.

I count them very carefully,
Especially 'round the moon,
Because I do not wish to go
To bed a star too soon.

HELEN COALE CREW.

## BROOM

Oh, all the ladies of the world
  When they are tired of play
They scrub the kitchens and the halls,
  They chase the dirt away.

But what would happen to them all
  If it were not for me,
They'd have to soil their dirty hands
  And bend upon the knee.

Oh, I'm the broom, the useful broom,
  I swish, I sweep, I sway,
I'm empress of the kitchen
  And the queen of cleaning day.

JOHN FARRAR.

## FATHER'S BIRTHDAY CAKE

When Father's birthday comes around
  We bake the biggest cake!
We sift and whip and sweeten it;
  Such trouble as we take!

For Mother says he works all day
  To buy us everything!
So when we make his birthday cake,
  Of course we laugh and sing.

Bobby beats and beats the eggs
  And Margy sifts the flour,
Bess and I chop raisins up,
  And bake it for an hour.

Then when at last the cake is done,
  We ice it all about,
And light a candle for each child,
  To let our love shine out!

ADA LORRAINE JEX.

## GRANDMOTHER'S GARDEN

Grandmother's garden had old-fashioned flowers,
  Hollyhocks, roses and rue,
And Grandmother dear, in her quaint little gown,
  Was an old-fashioned, sweet flower too.

MIRIAM OTT MUNSON.

## GOOD NIGHT

Good night! good night!
Far flies the light;

But still God's love
Shall flame above,
Making all bright.
Good night! Good night!

VICTOR HUGO.

## HER CHOICE

If I could not be the girl I am
With milk for tea, and bread and jam,
A bed to sleep in, warm and dry,
Not wet with dew, where crickets cry—
If I had to be a flower, I think
I'd love to be a rose—and pink!

MATTIE LEE HAUSGEN.

## HIPPITY HOP TO BED

O it's hippity hop to bed!
I'd rather sit up instead.
But when father says "must,"
There's nothing but just
Go hippity hop to bed.

LEROY JACKSON.

## THE GINGERBREAD MAN

Humpty Dumpty Dickery Dan,
   Sing heigh! sing ho! for the Gingerbread Man
With his form so neat,
   And his smile so sweet,
And his gingerbread shoes on his gingerbread feet.

His eyes are two currants, so round and so black
   He's baked in a pan lying flat on his back.

He comes from the oven so glossy and brown
  The finest gingerbread man in town.

And why is his gingerbread smile so sweet?
  And why is his gingerbread form so neat?
And why has he shoes on his gingerbread feet?
  Because he is made for my Teddy to eat.

EVA ROWLAND.

## LITTLE DANNY DONKEY

I hate to talk about it, 'cause
  it's sad enough for tears,
But—little Danny Donkey—didn't
  like to wash his ears!
At breakfast every morning
  Danny's Mother sent him back
To do his washing over 'cause
  his ears were simply *black!*
They say he's doing better now—
  and oh, I hope it's true!
I'd hate to be so lazy and so
  careless! Shouldn't you?

HELEN COWLES LE CRON.

## MISS T.[1]

It's a very odd thing—
  As odd as can be—
That whatever Miss T. eats
  Turns into Miss T.;
Porridge and apples,
  Mince, muffins and mutton,
Jam, junket, jumbles—
  Not a rap, not a button

[1] *From "Peacock Pie." By permission of Henry Holt & Co.*

It matters; the moment
They're out of her plate,
Though shared by Miss Butcher
And sour Mr. Bate,
Tiny and cheerful,
And neat as can be,
Whatever Miss T. eats
Turns into Miss T.

WALTER DE LA MARE.

## MIX A PANCAKE

Mix a pancake,
Stir a pancake,
Pop it in the pan;
Fry the pancake,
Toss the pancake,—
Catch it if you can.

CHRISTINA ROSSETTI.

## MOVIES IN THE FIRE

I like to sit here by the hearth,
I never, never tire
Of looking at the Movie Show
I see within the fire!

Sometimes I watch a fairy dance
In dress of crimson glow;
Sometimes the wind comes down and turns
The ashes into snow;

Sometimes I see a giant's head
With just one ugly eye;
Sometimes with driftwood, flames I change
To rainbows in the sky!

When Mother says the time has come
For children to retire
I'm loath to leave my cozy place
And the movies in the fire!

MILDRED D. SHACKLETT.

## NEW SHOES

I have new shoes in the Fall-time
And new ones in the Spring.
Whenever I wear my new shoes
I always have to sing!

ALICE WILKINS.

## OUR HOUSE

I like our house because it is so big and old,
With lots of places where I can go and hide
When I want to . . .
And an attic I can shut myself inside.

My room has one high window where I watch the moon
Leaking through the maples, and making
The concrete walk look like a river
Right in our backyard—
A silver river with black fishes swimming
In the shadows—
Just alive with little black fishes shaking
In the silver water . . .
It's funny that no one ever saw
That river before—
It drops out of sight at the basement door
I can hear it whispering under the floor,
It goes to China, I suppose,
But I'll never tell—and *nobody knows*
*Only me.*

I like our garden, too, it isn't set in rows,
But looks as if things happened just to grow
Right there that way . . .
And if a hollyhock comes up by chance beside a rose,
Not close enough to choke,
My mother lets it stay.
Sometimes at night when it is white and still
The garden shivers till the poppies spill
Their petals on the grass,
And once I saw a shadow pass over it—
It wasn't a shadow exactly because it was light,
And it wasn't a wind because it was still—
It's funny that nobody saw it come over the hill
And stop in our garden—*nobody knows*
*Only me* and I'll never tell.

NELLIE BURGET MILLER.

## POP-CORN LAND

One day we took a journey,
Down into pop-corn land,
To see the pop-corn children
And hear the pop-corn band.

The children all lay sleeping
Wrapped in their blankets brown,
The wire cradle rocked them
Quite gently up and down.

The band awoke them playing
With a gay and tuneful pop.
Then each one jumped up quickly
To join the noisy hop.

Their dresses white and fluffy
Spread airy sails around
As they danced, and skipped, and floated,
To the pop-pop-popping sound.

ELSIE F. KARTACK.

## SEWING

If Mother Nature patches
  The leaves of trees and vines,
I'm sure she does her darning
  With the needles of the pines;
They are so long and slender,
  And somewhere in full view,
She has her threads of cobwebs,
  And a thimbleful of dew.

UNKNOWN.

## SHE WOULD

A kite and a string
Is the sort of a thing
That I'd like to be if I could.
I'd sail everywhere
In the bonnie blue air,
And hunt up the man-in-the-moon,
I would!

Of course in the sky
I might sail very high!
But I wouldn't care if I should!
For always I'd know
That wherever I'd go,
My mother'd hold on to the string,
She would!

DIXIE WILLSON.

## SMELLS (Junior)

My Daddy smells like tobacco and books
Mother, like lavender and listerine,

Uncle John carries a smell of cigars,
Nannie smells starchy and soapy and clean.

Shandy, my dog, has a smell of his own
(When he's been out in the rain he smells most),
But Katie, the cook, is more splendid than all;
She smells exactly like hot buttered toast.

CHRISTOPHER MORLEY.

## THE BABY'S DANCE

Dance, little baby, dance up high:
  Never mind, baby, mother is by;
Crow and caper, caper and crow,
  There, little baby, there you go;
Up to the ceiling, down to the ground,
  Backwards and forwards, round and round:
Then dance, little baby, and mother shall sing,
  While the gay merry coral goes ding, ding-
    a-ding, ding.

ANN TAYLOR.

## THE CUCKOO CLOCK

The cuckoo in the clock by day
Is usually very gay;
And that's because with people near,
There's not a thing for him to fear,
But when the sitting room is dim
And there's no one to welcome him,
How tremblingly he must come out
To flap his wings and look about.
Why, only just the other night
The cuckoo stopped the clock from fright.

JOHN FARRAR.

## THE DAYS OF THE WEEK

Monday is a good day
It has no special plan;
Tuesday is our washing day,
And Wednesday's cleaning man.
On Thursday nurse is always out;
On Friday Grandma's here,
It's tomorrow day that strikes me
As the funniest of the year.

Saturday's a good day,
With peanuts, walks and such,
With bright balloons along the park,
I like it very much;
With thousands, maybe millions,
Of babies large and small,
Just like a giant party
With Maypoles on the Mall.

Sunday's such a different day,
When Daddy stays with me.
We sing and read and sometimes walk,
And friends and friends for tea.
But there is also yesterday,
A most peculiar one,
It's always gone, it never comes—
And just remembers fun.

But it's tomorrow puzzles me;
It never comes or goes.
Just what it is they won't explain;
I think that no one knows.
Perhaps it is a dreamy thing,
A bubble gone away;
Perhaps it's put together from
Two halves of yesterday.

When I grow up I'll find it
And do the things I plan;
I'll be a digger in the street,
I'll be a taxi-man.
I'll crowd all good things I can think—
No writing nor any sums;
I'll have a glorious picnic—
If tomorrow ever comes!

JOHN FARRAR.

## THE POPCORN PARTY

In little white dresses and little white pants
Girl fairies, boy fairies join in the dance,
One-stepping, waltzing, faster and higher,
On a floor made of holes, over red and gold fire!

E. R. B.

## THE TYPEWRITER

It talks and talks, but the words
It writes so clear and black.
It writes my name, T-O-M, Tom!
But says just tick, tick, tack.

It's quite unlike the telephone,
Which does not chatter so,
But kindly calls for us to hear
The things we need to know.

MRS. SCHUYLER VAN RENSSELAER.

## THE ZIGZAG BOY AND GIRL

I know a little zigzag boy,
   Who goes this way and that;
He never knows just where he puts
   His coat or shoes or hat.

I know a little zigzag girl,
  Who flutters here and there;
She never knows just where to find
  Her brush to fix her hair.

If you are not a zigzag child,
  You'll have no cause to say
That you forgot, for you will know
  Where things are put away.

UNKNOWN.

## A TALE FROM THE GARDEN

There was a Slug who ate and ate,
He ate when dry, he ate when wet;
He ate the asters and the stocks,
And gobbled up tall hollyhocks,
And as for lupins and pentstemon
He was a perfect little demon;
The choicest rose or rare carnation
Were swallowed without hesitation,
In fact, I think it can be said
Each day he cleared a flower-bed.

One morn a hungry Thrush espied
The greedy Slug—and he died—
Down went the Slug, down Thrush's throat,
But what you really ought to note
Is: First fat Slug eats all the flowers
And then the Thrush the Slug devours,
Think a moment: what a lot
Inside him, now, the Thrush has got!
Beds of asters, rows of stocks,
Single, double hollyhocks,
Pinks, pentstemon, lupin, rose,
Almost every flower that grows,
BUT, this comfort let us hug,
HE HAS ALSO GOT THE SLUG!

MARGARET WYNNE JONES.

## AN EXPLANATION OF THE GRASSHOPPER

The Grasshopper, the Grasshopper,
I will explain to you:—
He is the Brownies' racehorse,
The fairies' Kangaroo.

VACHEL LINDSAY.

## BUMBLE-BEE AND CLOVER

Came a roaring bumble-bee,
Pockets full of money.
"Ah, good morning, Clover sweet,
What's the price of honey?"

"Help yourself, sir," Clover said,
"Bumble, you're too funny;
Never Clover yet so poor
She must sell her honey."

UNKNOWN.

## CAROLINE CRICKET

Miss Caroline Cricket
Hopped out of a thicket
And sang a most pitiful ditty;
Some gay butterflies
Had made fun of her eyes
And said that her clothes were not pretty.

" 'Tis no use to be vain
For I know I am plain,
Just a plain little dull brown cricket;
But maybe my song
Will cheer some one along,"
So she sang and she sang in the thicket.

C. LINDSAY MC COY.

## COBWEBS

Dainty fairy lace-work, O so finely spun,
Lying on the grasses and shining in the sun,
Guess the fairies washed you and spread you out to dry,
And left you there, a-glistening and a-shining to the sky!

UNKNOWN.

## CRICKETS

What makes the crickets "crick" all night
  And never stop to rest?
They must take naps in daytime
  So at night they'll "crick" their best.
I wonder if they just take turns
  And try to make it rhyme,
Or do a million crickets
  Keep "cricking" all the time?

HELEN WING.

## DEVIL'S DARNING NEEDLE

I saw the Devil's Darning Needle
Out in that bed of phlox;
My heart is going pit-a-pat
  For
    There
      Is
        A
          Hole
            In
              My
                Socks!

C. LINDSAY MC COY.

## FIREFLIES

Little lamps of the dusk
You fly low and gold
When the summer evening
Starts to unfold.
So that all the insects,
Now, before you pass,
Will have light to see by
Undressing in the grass.

But when the night has flowered,
Little lamps agleam,
You fly over tree-tops
Following a dream.
Men wonder from their windows
That a firefly goes so far.
They do not know your longing
To be a shooting star.

CAROLYN HALL.

## FIREFLIES

I like to chase the fireflies,
  Chase them to and fro;
I like to watch them dart about,
  Their little lamps aglow.

In the evening's twilight dim
  I follow them about;
I often think I have one caught,
  And then his light goes out.

I cannot tell just where he is
  Until he winks, you see,
Then far away I see his light,
  He's played a joke on me.

GRACE WILSON COPLEN.

## FIREFLY

A little light is going by,
Is going up to see the sky
A little light with wings.

I never could have thought of it,
To have a little bug all lit
And made to go on wings.

ELIZABETH MADOX ROBERTS.

## GRASSHOPPER GREEN

Grasshopper Green is a comical chap;
He lives on the best of fare.
Bright little trousers, jacket, and cap,
These are his summer wear.
Out in the meadow he loves to go,
Playing away in the sun;
It's hopperty, skipperty, high and low,
Summer's the time for fun.

Grasshopper Green has a quaint little house;
It's under the hedge so gay.
Grandmother Spider, as still as a mouse,
Watches him over the way.
Gladly he's calling the children, I know,
Out in the beautiful sun;
It's hopperty, skipperty, high and low,
Summer's the time for fun.

UNKNOWN.

## HONEY BEE

The "Honey Bee," its habitat
We study with a zest;
We like to see her at her work
But never as a guest.

"Queen Bee" is mother of them all,
She animates the hive.
Her subjects are so true to her
And that is why they thrive.

The "Drone Bees" are the gentlemen
They roam the fields and sing;
They never bring in honey and
Indeed they never sting.

The "Worker Bee" has her own style
Different from the queen;
Her body is much stouter,
Her eyes are very keen.

Her pointed tongue is like a tube,
She sips the flowers gay;
Much like we sip our lemonade,
On some hot summer day.

Her pockets are upon the leg
And look like tiny sacs;
In some she keeps her pollen dust,
In some she keeps her wax.

She only lives a few short weeks,
This famous "Worker Bee"
But she always will be quoted,
For thrift and industry.

C. LINDSAY MC COY.

## HORNETS

Mac and Daisy, Carl and Marie,
Found this nest in an old hollow tree:
They made good time on the way back—
Carl and Marie, Daisy and Mac.

Hornets above, below, around,
Pitter patter over the ground,
Helter
Skelter
They Went
Pell Mell—
Some were stung, but soon got well.

C. LINDSAY MC COY.

## KATY-DID

The Katy-did's note
Is not made in her throat—
She has a peculiar style;
She simply sings by rubbing her wings
And is heard one-fourth of a mile.
Katy did—she did—she did—
But some say Katy didn't.

C. LINDSAY MCCOY.

## LADY-BIRD

Lady-bird, lady-bird! fly away home!
The field-mouse has gone to her nest,
The daisies have shut up their sleepy red eyes,
And the bees and the birds are at rest.

Lady-bird, lady-bird! fly away home!
The glow-worm is lighting her lamp,
The dew's falling fast, and your fine speckled wings
Will flag with the close-clinging damp.

Lady-bird, lady-bird! fly away home!
The fairy bells tinkle afar!
Make haste, or they'll catch you, and harness you fast
With a cobweb to Oberon's car.

CAROLINE B. SOUTHEY.

## LADY BUG

The Lady Bug is a beautiful bug
  Some red, some yellow, some brown.
I pray you take note
  Of her glossy coat
And see the black spots on her gown.

The Lady Bug is a most useful bug
  Killing the tiny green flies,
For the flies will eat
  The leaves and the wheat,
The fruit and the flowers we prize.

C. LINDSAY MC COY.

## MISTER ANGLEWORM

After the rain comes on the lawn
And all the thunder clouds are gone
The dirt lifts up beneath the fern
And out comes Mister Angleworm.

He humps his back, then lengthens out
And pokes his pointed nose about.
He loves to roll and stretch and squirm
This lazy Mister Angleworm.

Then Mrs. Robin hops along
For she knows where good worms belong,
She gives her head a saucy turn
And down goes Mister Angleworm.

MANCHESTER.

## OLD DAME CRICKET

Old Dame Cricket, down in the thicket,
Brought up her children nine,—
Queer little chaps, in glossy black caps
And brown little suits so fine.

"My children," she said,
"The birds are abed:
Go and make the dark earth glad!
Chirp while you can!"
And then she began,—
Till, oh, what a concert they had!

They hopped with delight
They chirped all night,
Singing, "Cheer up! cheer up! cheer!"
Old Dame Cricket,
Down in the thicket,
Sat awake till dawn to hear.

UNKNOWN.

## SINGING

Little birds sing with their beaks
In the apple trees;
But little crickets in the grass
Are singing with their knees.

DOROTHY ALDIS.

## SUCH WISDOM

Though tiny things, ants must see very well;
They must have been carefully taught how to smell;

Because when my mother makes cookies or pie
They find out about it much sooner than I!

UNKNOWN.

## THE BEETLE

The other day to my surprise,
I saw a little beetle blue
Spread slowly out, and fly away—
I never thought he flew.

I see, he wears an overall
To shield his gauzy wings,
As I put on a pinafore
To save my Sunday things.

EDITH KING.

## THE BUTTERFLY

Up and down the air you float
Like a little fairy boat;
I should like to sail the sky,
Gliding like a butterfly!

CLINTON SCOLLARD.

## THE CATERPILLAR [1]

Brown and furry
Caterpillar in a hurry;
Take your walk
To the shady leaf or stalk.
May no toad spy you;
May the little birds pass you;
Spin and die,
To live again a butterfly.

CHRISTINA ROSSETTI.

[1] *From "Sing Song." By permission of the Macmillan Co.*

## THE CHIRRUPY CRICKET

There's a chirrupy cricket as guest in my room,
He's quiet all day, but at night in the gloom
With a *zip* on the hearth and a *zup* at the door,
The chirrupy cricket hops out on the floor.

He's black and he's shiny, he's not very fat,
He's sleek as the silk of my father's tall hat;
He skates and skedaddles on carpet and rug,
And seems an extremely well-bred little bug.

And when I'm alone in my room every night,
And the shadows have come, and the moon's out of sight,
And the world is all silent and solemn and bare,
I'm glad that my chirrupy cricket is there!

MARTHA B. THOMAS.

## THE SPIDER AND THE FLY

"Will you walk into my parlor?"
  Said the Spider to the Fly;
" 'Tis the prettiest little parlor
  That ever you did spy.

"The way into my parlor
  Is up a winding stair,
And I have many curious things
  To show when you are there."

"Oh, no, no," said the little Fly,
  "To ask me is in vain;
For who goes up your winding stair
  Can ne'er come down again."

"I'm sure you must be weary, dear,
  With soaring up so high;
Will you rest upon my little bed?"
  Said the Spider to the Fly.

"There are pretty curtains drawn around;
  The sheets are fine and thin,
And if you like to rest awhile,
  I'll snugly tuck you in!"

"Oh, no, no," said the little Fly,
  "For I've often heard it said,
They never, never wake again,
  Who sleep upon your bed."

Said the cunning Spider to the Fly:
  "Dear friend, what can I do
To prove the warm affection
  I've always felt for you?

"I have within my pantry
  Good store of all that's nice:
I'm sure you're very welcome—
  Will you please to take a slice?"

"Sweet creature!" said the Spider,
  "You're witty and you're wise;
How handsome are your gauzy wings:
  How brilliant are your eyes!

"I have a little looking-glass
  Upon my parlor shelf;
If you'll step in one moment, dear,
  You shall behold yourself."

"I thank you, gentle sir," she said,
  "For what you're pleased to say,
And, bidding you good-morning now,
  I'll call another day."

The Spider turned him round about,
  And went into his den,
For well he knew the silly Fly
  Would soon come back again:

So he wove a subtle web
  In a little corner sly,
And set his table ready
  To dine upon the Fly.

Then came out to his door again,
  And merrily did sing:
"Come hither, hither, pretty Fly,
  With the pearl and silver wing;

"Your robes are green and purple—
  There's a crest upon your head;
Your eyes are like the diamond bright,
  But mine are dull as lead!"

Alas, alas! how very soon
  This silly little Fly,
Hearing his wily, flattering words,
  Came slowly flittering by;

With buzzing wings she hung aloft,
  Then near and nearer drew,
Thinking only of her brilliant eyes,
  And green and purple hue—

Thinking only of her creasted head—
  Poor, foolish thing! At last,
Up jumped the cunning Spider,
  And fiercely held her fast.

He dragged her up his winding stair,
  Into his dismal den,
Within his little parlor—
  But she ne'er came out again.

And now, dear little children,
  Who may this story read,
To idle, silly, flattering words,
  I pray you ne'er give heed.

Unto an evil counsellor
  Close heart and ear and eye,
And take a lesson from this tale
  Of the Spider and the Fly.

MARY HOWITT.

## THE SPIDER WEB

How does a spider ever weave
His web so fine? I do believe
*He dreams* it in the night, as I
Dream of the fairies when I lie
In bed. Well, anyway, it seems
As soft and fine as fairy dreams!

MATTIE LEE HAUSGEN.

## THE SPIDER'S WEB

Spider! Spider!
  What are you spinning?
A cloak for a fairy
  I'm just beginning.

What is it made of,
  Tell me true?
Threads of moonshine
  And pearls of dew.

When will the fairy
  Be wearing it?
Tonight, when the glow-worm
  Lamps are lit.

Can I see her
  If I come peeping?
All good children
  Must be then sleeping.

CHARLOTTE DRUIT COLE.

## THE WORM

Dickie found a broken spade
And said he'd dig himself a well,
And then Charles took a piece of tin,
And I was digging with a shell.

Then Will said he would dig one too;
We shaped them out and made them wide,
And I dug up a piece of clod
That had a little worm inside.

We watched him pucker up himself
And stretched himself to walk away.
He tried to go inside the dirt,
But Dickie made him wait and stay.

His shining skin was soft and wet.
I poked him once to see him squirm,
And then Will said, "I wonder if
He knows that he's a worm."

And then we sat back on our feet
And wondered for a little bit,
And we forgot to dig our wells
A while, and tried to answer it.

And while we tried to find it out
He puckered in a little wad
And then he stretched himself again
And went back home inside the clod.

ELIZABETH MADOX ROBERTS.

## WHIRLIGIG BEETLE

Here, if you please, is a Whirligig
Dressed in a blue-black middy;
He whirls about on the water top,
Acting strange and giddy.

He cannot breathe as the fishes do
And so he must take great care
To carry with him under his wing,
A tiny bubble of air.

C. LINDSAY MC COY.

## A FARMER WENT TROTTING

A farmer went trotting upon a gray mare,
Bumpety, bumpety, bump!
With his daughter behind him, so rosy and fair,
Lumpety, lumpety, lump!

OLD RHYME.

## ALAS, ALACK! [1]

Ann, Ann!
Come! quick as you can!
There's a fish that *talks*
In the frying pan.
Out of the fat,
As clear as glass,
He put up his mouth
And moaned "Alas!"
Oh, most mournful,
"Alas, alack!"

[1] *From "Peacock Pie." By permission of Henry Holt & Co.*

Then turned to his sizzling,
And sank him back.

WALTER DE LA MARE.

## HOT WEATHER

I never saw a puppy that
Wore a little streamer hat.

I never met a rabbit who
Had a dress of pink or blue.

I never saw a squirrel trail
Hair ribbons upon his tail.

And nobody has ever heard
Of shirt and panties on a bird!

Oh, why must I, however hot,
Wear EVERYTHING that they do not?

DOROTHY ALDIS.

Little Jerry Hall, he was so small,
A rat could eat him—hat and all.

UNKNOWN.

P double inkin—P double I
P double inkin—Pumpkin pie.

UNKNOWN.

## THE JUMBLIES

They went to sea in a sieve, they did;
In a sieve they went to sea:

In spite of all their friends could say,
On a winter's morn, on a stormy day,
In a sieve they went to sea.
And when the sieve turned round and round,
And every one cried, "You'll all be drowned!"
They called aloud, "Our sieve ain't big;
But we don't care a button; we don't care a fig:
In a sieve we'll go to sea!
Far and few, far and few,
Are the lands where the Jumblies live;
Their heads are green, and their hands are blue;
And they went to sea in a sieve.

They sailed away in a sieve, they did,
In a sieve they sailed so fast,
With only a beautiful pea-green veil
Tied with a ribbon, by way of a sail,
To a small tobacco-pipe mast.
And every one said who saw them go,
"Oh! won't they soon be upset, you know?
For the sky is dark, and the voyage is long,
And, happen what may, it's extremely wrong
In a sieve to sail so fast."
Far and few, far and few,
Are the lands where the Jumblies live;
Their heads are green, and their hands are blue;
And they went to sea in a sieve.

The water it soon came in, it did;
The water it soon came in:
So, to keep them dry, they wrapped their feet
In a pinky paper all folded neat;
And they fastened it down with a pin.
And they passed the night in a crockery jar:
And each of them said, "How wise we are!
Though the sky be dark, and the voyage be long,
Yet we never can think we were rash or wrong,
While round in our sieve we spin."

Far and few, far and few,
Are the lands where the Jumblies live;
Their heads are green, and their hands are blue;
And they went to sea in a sieve.

And all night long they sailed away;
And when the sun went down,
They whistled and warbled a moony song,
To the echoing sound of a moony gong,
In the shade of the mountains brown.
"O Timballoo! How happy we are
When we live in a sieve and a crockery jar!
All night long, in the moonlight pale,
We sail away with a pea-green sail
In the shade of the mountains brown."
Far and few, far and few,
Are the lands where the Jumblies live;
Their heads are green, and their hands are blue;
And they went to sea in a sieve.

They sailed to the Western Sea, they did,—
To a land all covered with trees;
And they bought an owl, and a useful cart,
And a pound of rice, and a cranberry tart,
And a hive of silvery bees;
And they bought a pig, and some green jackdaws,
And a lovely monkey with lollipop paws,
And forty bottles of ring-bo-ree,
And no end of Stilton cheese.
Far and few, far and few,
Are the lands where the Jumblies live;
Their heads are green, and their hands are blue;
And they went to sea in a sieve.

And in twenty years they all came back,—
In twenty years or more;
And every one said, "How tall they've grown!
For they've been to the Lakes, and the Torrible Zone,

And the hills of the Chankly Bore."
And they drank their health, and gave them a feast
Of dumpling made of beautiful yeast;
And every one said, "If we only live,
We, too, will go to sea in a sieve,
To the hills of the Chankly Bore."
Far and few, far and few,
Are the lands where the Jumblies live;
Their heads are green, and their hands are blue;
And they went to sea in a sieve.

EDWARD LEAR.

The monkey put Puss in the cook's dinner pot,
But Puss wouldn't stay there, because it was hot.

UNKNOWN.

## THE PEACH

There once was a peach on a tree,
The fairest you ever did see.
But it ripened too fast,
Till it fell down at last,
And turned to a squash! O dear me!

ABBIE FARWELL BROWN.

## THE QUANGLE WANGLE'S HAT

### I

On the top of the Crumpety Tree
The Quangle Wangle sat,
But his face you could not see,
On account of his Beaver Hat.
For his hat was a hundred and two feet wide,
With ribbons and bibbons on every side,
And bells, and buttons, and loops, and lace,
So that nobody ever could see the face
Of the Quangle Wangle Quee.

II

The Quangle Wangle said
   To himself on the Crumpety Tree,
"Jam, and jelly, and bread
   Are the best of food for me!
But the longer I live on this Crumpety Tree
The plainer than ever it seems to me
That very few people come this way
And that life on the whole is far from gay!"
      Said the Quangle Wangle Quee.

III

But there came to the Crumpety Tree
   Mr. and Mrs. Canary;
And they said, "Did ever you see
   Any spot so charmingly airy?
May we build a nest on your lovely Hat?
Mr. Quangle Wangle, grant us that!
Oh, please let us come and build a nest
Of whatever material suits you best,
      Mr. Quangle Wangle Quee!"

IV

And besides, to the Crumpety Tree
   Came the Stork, the Duck, and the Owl;
The Snail and the Bumble-Bee,
   The Frog and the Fimble Fowl
(The Fimble Fowl, with a corkscrew leg);
And all of them said, "We humbly beg
We may build our homes on your lovely Hat,—
Mr. Quangle Wangle, grant us that!
      Mr. Quangle Wangle Quee!"

V

And the Golden Grouse came there,
   And the Pobble who has no toes,

And the small Olympian bear,
  And the Dong with the luminous nose.
And the Blue Babbon who played the flute,
And the Orient Calf from the Land of Tute,
And the Attery Squash, and the Bisky Bat,—
All came and built on the lovely Hat
    Of the Quangle Wangle Quee.

VI

And the Quangle Wangle said
  To himself on the Crumpety Tree,
"When all these creatures move
  What a wonderful noise there will be!"
And at night by the light of the mulberry moon
They danced to the flute of the Blue Baboon,
On the broad green leaves of the Crumpety Tree,
And all were as happy as happy could be,
    With the Quangle Wangle Quee.

EDWARD LEAR.

## THE SALT AND PEPPER DANCE

One day, or no, one night—
  It happened just by chance
The Salt and Pepper pots
  Decided they should dance.

They skipped and skupped about
  As merry as could be,
For Salt and Pepper pots
  So *seldom* dance, you see.

They jigged and jumped and jogged—
  They really did too much—
The pepper sprinkled out
  And made them sneeze "Ker-SNUTCH!"

"Ker-Wish! Ker-Wash! Ker-Chow!"
  The dancers now were through.
"We'll have to stop," they said.
  "We'll have to st—Ker-Choo!"

WYMOND GARTHWAITE.

There was an old man who said, "How
Shall I flee from this horrible cow?
  I will sit on this stile
  And continue to smile,
Which may soften the heart of the cow."

EDWARD LEAR.

There was a young lady whose bonnet
Came untied when the birds sat upon it.
  Said she, "I don't care;
  All the birds in the air
Are welcome to sit on my bonnet."

EDWARD LEAR.

## WHEN I WAS A LITTLE BOY

When I was a little boy,
  I lived by myself;
And all the bread and cheese I got
  I put upon a shelf.
The rats and the mice—
  They led me such a life
I had to go to London
  To get myself a wife.

The streets were so bad,
  All the roads were so narrow,
I had to bring her home
  In a little wheebarrow.
The wheelbarrow broke,
  And my wife had a fall.

Down tumbled wheelbarrow,
Little wife and all.

OLD ENGLISH RHYME.

## A ROCK-A-BYE SONG

It's cuddle-me-time by the nursery clock
For turn-out-the-light-time is near
And just 'round the corner a velvety dream
Is waiting to meet you, my dear.

So rock-a-bye here
And rock-a-bye there
In a crickety-creakety rock-a-bye chair;
Then rock-a-bye that way
Then rock-a-bye this
And pay for the ride with a rock-a-bye kiss.

It's tuck-me-in-time by the nursery clock
For it's half-past-going-to-bed,
And soon it will be a quarter-to-sleep
For each little tired little head.

So rock-a-bye near
And rock-a-bye far
And follow the trail of the rock-a-bye star;
Then rock-a-bye softly
And rock-a-bye still
To rock-a-bye-baby-land over the hill.

HELEN WING.

## CHILD'S EVENSONG

Oh, the sky is so blue,
And the sun is so warm,
And the clouds sail so slowly along;
Oh, the flowers are so sweet,

And the birds are so gay,
And the trees are so tall and so strong;

Oh, the stars are so bright,
And the moon is so high,
And the wind sings so gentle a song;
Oh, my supper's so good,
And my bed is so soft,
I am glad, mother dear, all day long!

ETHEL ROBB.

## CHINESE LULLABY

Chinese Sandmen,
Wise and creepy,
Croon dream-songs
To make us sleepy.
A Chinese maid with slanting eyes
Is queen of all their lullabies.
On her ancient moon-guitar
She strums a sleep-song to a star;
And when big China-shadows fall
Snow-white lilies hear her call.
Chinese Sandmen,
Wise and creepy,
Croon dream-songs
To make us sleepy.

UNKNOWN.

## EVENING SONG[1]

Little child, good child, go to sleep
The tree-toads purr and the peepers peep;
Under the apple-tree grass grows deep;
Little child, good child, go to sleep!

[1] *From "Crack o' Dawn." By permission of the Macmillan Co.*

Big star out in the orange west;
Orioles swing in their gypsy nest;
Soft wind singing what you love best;
  Rest till the sunrise; rest, child, rest!

Swift dreams swarm in a silver flight—
Hand in hand with the sleepy night.
Lie down soft with your eyelids tight—
  Hush, child, little child, hush—
    good night.

FANNIE STEARNS DAVIS.

## GAELIC LULLABY

Hush! the waves are rolling in,
  White with foam, white with foam;
Father toils amid the din;
  But baby sleeps at home.

Hush! the winds roar hoarse and deep,—
  On they come, on they come!
Brother seeks the wandering sheep:
  But baby sleeps at home.

Hush! the rain sweeps over the knowes,
  Where they roam, where they roam;
Sister goes to seek the cows;
  But baby sleeps at home.

UNKNOWN.

## SLEEP, BABY, SLEEP

  Sleep, baby, sleep!
  Thy father watches his sheep;
Thy mother is shaking the dreamland tree,
And down falls a little dream on thee.
  Sleep, baby, sleep!

Sleep, baby, sleep!
The large stars are the sheep;
The little stars are the lambs I guess;
And the bright moon is the shepherdess.
Sleep, baby, sleep!

FROM THE GERMAN.

## SWEET AND LOW

Sweet and low, sweet and low,
Wind of the western sea,
Low, low, breathe and blow,
Wind of the western sea!
Over the rolling waters go,
Come from the dying moon, and blow,
Blow him again to me;
While my little one, while my pretty one sleeps.

Sleep and rest, sleep and rest,
Father will come to thee soon;
Rest, rest, on mother's breast,
Father will come to thee soon;
Father will come to his babe in the nest,
Silver sails all out of the west
Under the silver moon:
Sleep, my little one, sleep, my pretty one, sleep.

ALFRED TENNYSON.

## A SOMETIMES WISH

Sometimes,
I wish I knew the magic word
To change myself into a bird,
I'd fly to places far away

Where summer stays the whole year round
And juicy oranges are found
And children on the beaches play—
Where red poinsettias wave in the breeze
And long, gray moss hangs draped from trees,
Where there's no snow but *shells* instead;
But long before the day should wane
I'd wish to fly back home again
And creep into my own small bed!

MILDRED D. SHACKLETT.

## CITY LIGHTS [1]

Into the endless dark
The lights of the buildings shine,
Row upon twinkling row,
Line upon glistening line.
Up and up they mount
Till the tallest seems to be
The topmost taper set
On a towering Christmas tree.

RACHEL LYMAN FIELD.

## DAYS

Some days my thoughts are just cocoons—all cold, and dull, and blind,
They hang from dripping branches in the grey woods of my mind;

And other days they drift and shine—such free and flying things!
I find the gold-dust in my hair, left by their brushing wings.

KARLE WILSON BAKER.

[1] *From "Pointed People." By permission of the Macmillan Co.*

## MAGIC WAVES

Radio waves coming over the air
Are magic waves that fairies share
With grown-ups and with children, too.
Does it not seem wonderful to you?

GERTRUDE VAN WINKLE.

## MY RADIO

My radio set is very small
It takes hardly any room at all.
It's not like Daddy's great big set
Just any station he can get
But mine, you see, is my very own
And I can listen when I'm all alone.

GERTRUDE VAN WINKLE.

## SKYSCRAPERS [1]

Do skyscrapers ever grow tired
Of holding themselves up high?
Do they ever shiver on frosty nights
With their tops against the sky?
Do they feel lonely sometimes
Because they have grown so tall?
Do they ever wish they could lie right down
And never get up at all?

RACHEL LYMAN FIELD.

## STATIC

Hear that crickley, crackley static.
Perhaps it's fairies in our attic.

GERTRUDE VAN WINKLE.

[1] *From "Pointed People." By permission of the Macmillan Co.*

## THE MICROPHONE

The microphone is a funny thing.
It stands so still and tall.
Before it one must play or sing
Or it won't work at all.

GERTRUDE VAN WINKLE.

## THE TELEGRAPH [1]

The wires spread out far and wide,
And cross the town and countryside,
They cross through deserts and through snows,
And pass the spots where no one goes.

But though no feet go out that way
A million words go every day;
Along the wires everywhere
A million words flash through the air.

And if we're happy, if we're well,
The wires far away can tell,
The little words can cross all space
And talk to friends in any place.

ANNETTE WYNNE.

The wires are so still and high [1]
We never hear the words go by,
Yet messages fly far and near—
I wonder if the birds can hear.

And when they perch on wires and sing,
I wonder are they listening,

[1] *Reprinted by permission from "For Days and Days." Copyright, 1919, by Frederick A. Stokes Co.*

And telling out to earth and sky
A lovely word is going by?

ANNETTE WYNNE.

## THRENODY

The red leaves fall upon the lake,
The brown leaves drift,
The yellow leaves fly with the wind,
High and swift.

And Autumn nights bring open fires,
With roasted corn,
When silver frosted grasses greet
Early morn.

I fly my kite across the hill,
The slim string breaks,
It flashes like a cloud above
Hills and lakes.

I cannot follow, only stand
And watch it go,
Across the far and lonely place
That airplanes know.

JOHN FARRAR.

## THE BAND

When the band comes along the street
Sometimes it does not play. The drum
Monotonously goes tum-tum, tum-tum, tumpety-tum
To mark the time for marching feet.

But presently a tiny sound
One trumpet makes: and all around

The music things are raised, and then
I know the band will play again.

And suddenly, as thunder comes
The horns and trumpets, flutes and drums
Crash into glorious noise that breaks
All over me in little shakes.

And all inside me seems to swell
With feelings that I cannot tell
And I am glad: I can't see why
Just then I *almost* want to cry.

But when the band is out of sight
And I can hear it far away,
It sounds as my tin bandsmen might
If they could really play.

JOHN.

## WHISTLES

I want to learn to whistle.
I've always wanted to.
I fix my mouth to do it but
The whistle won't come through.

I think perhaps it's stuck, and so
I try it once again.
Can people swallow whistles?
Where is my whistle then?

DOROTHY ALDIS.

## A PREFERENCE

Some children like gay weather
When the world is dry for play;

But that's so quiet and stupid,
  I like a windy day;

When the gray clouds hide the sky,
  And the furry white clouds sink low,
And the thunder-heads tumble over the hill
  From where, I don't quite know;

When small drops rustle the leaves,
  And large drops bend the flowers,
Pounding the dusty turnpike—
  Rain, rain—for hours and hours,

Till the big brooks jump down the mountain,
  And the little brooks cover the plain,
Oh, yes, I like the rainy days,
  When the world is clean again.

JOHN FARRAR.

## A RAINY DAY

We always like a rainy day,
When we must stay indoors to play,
For there are many things to do,
That make a lovely day for you.

With dolls to dress and books to read,
Our kitten and the dog to feed,—
And oh, it is such fun to think
The flowers are asking for a drink.

Sometimes we sing our dolls to sleep
Before the fire—and then we keep
Quite still, as on the rug we lie—
They never waken up nor cry.

Close by the window we all wait,
And watch for Daddy when he's late;
We look right through the rain—and then—
We see him coming home again!

EMILIE BLACKMORE STAPP.

## AT NIGHT

When I go to bed at night
The darkness is a bear.
He crouches in the corner,
Or hides behind a chair;
The one who tells me stories—
She does not know he's there.

But when she kisses me good-night,
And darkness starts to creep
Across the floor, why, then I see
It's just a woolly sheep,
That nibbles at my rugs awhile
Before we go to sleep.

ANNE BLACKWELL PAYNE.

## BROADCASTING

Last night the thunder began to roll
And I began to cry,
Then Daddy said, "That's broadcasting, Child,
From Station SKY!
'A storm is coming,' the thunder says,
So step inside real quick,
We'll watch the lightning's fireworks play
And hear the wind's music."

I'll not be frightened at all next year
When March comes blowing by

And Daddy and I tune in again
With Station SKY!

MILDRED D. SHACKLETT.

## BROOMS

On stormy days
When the wind is high
Tall trees are brooms
Sweeping the sky.

They swish their branches
In buckets of rain,
And swash and sweep it
Blue again.

DOROTHY ALDIS.

## CLOUDS

Over the hill the clouds race by
Playing tag in a blue, blue sky;
Some are fat and some are thin
And one old cloud has a double-chin;

One is a girl with up-turned nose
And one wears slippers with pointed toes;
There's a puppy-dog too with a bumpety tail
And a farmer boy with his milking pail.

Sometimes they jumble all in a mass
And get tangled up with others that pass
As over the hill they go racing by
Playing tag in a blue, blue sky.

HELEN WING.

## CORAL [1]

O sailor, come ashore,
  What have you brought for me?
Red coral, white coral,
  Coral from the sea.

I did not dig it from the ground,
  Nor pluck it from a tree;
Feeble insects made it
  In the stormy sea.

CHRISTINA ROSSETTI.

## ECHO

I sometimes wonder where he lives,
  This Echo that I never see.
I hear his voice now in the hedge,
  Then down behind the willow tree.

And when I call, "Oh, please come out,"
  "Come out," he always quick replies.
"Hello, hello," again I say:
  "Hello, hello," he softly cries.

He must be jolly, Echo must,
  For when I laugh, "Ho, ho, ho, ho,"
Like any other friendly boy,
  He answers me with "Ho, ho, ho."

I think perhaps he'd like to play;
  I know some splendid things to do.
He must be lonely hiding there;
  I wouldn't like it. Now, would you?

UNKNOWN.

[1] *From "Sing Song.' By permission of the Macmillan Co.*

## FAIRY CARPETS

Pine needle carpets and crisp brown leaves
And carpets of velvet moss;
Are laid in the woods for the narrow feet
Of fairies to walk across.
And even the smallest fairy knows,
When it rains she must never wet her toes.

ANNE BLACKWELL PAYNE.

## FALLING SNOW

See the pretty snowflakes
Falling from the sky;
On the walk and housetop
Soft and thick they lie.

On the window-ledges
On the branches bare;
Now how fast they gather,
Filling all the air.

Look into the garden,
Where the grass was green;
Covered by the snowflakes,
Not a blade is seen.

Now the bare black bushes
All look soft and white,
Every twig is laden—
What a pretty sight!

ANONYMOUS.

## FOG[1]

The fog comes
on little cat feet

It sits looking
over harbor and city
on silent haunches
and then moves on.

CARL SANDBURG.

## FOR APRIL SHOWERS

When I was small I hated rain
But never do I now complain;

I'm old enough to own a set—
Cape and umbrella for the wet;

In such a lovely shade of red
It's very rosy overhead,

And when the raindrops pelt and patter
Upon my cape, it doesn't matter.

So all these April showers, you see,
Are just a lot of fun for me!

EMILY ROSE BURT.

## FROST

Frost is an elf
With a crystal wand;
She waves it once
And freezes a pond.

[1] *From "Chicago Poems." By permission of Henry Holt & Co.*

She waves it twice—
A bare black tree
Is turned
To loveliest filigree.

Three times—fern leaves
And shadowy boughs
Are etched on the panes
Of every house.

ETHEL ROMIG FULLER.

## IF I—

I think if I were a tree
I'd like to grow down by the sea—
My shadow could then all the day
On the waves and the tides dance and play
With the spray—

And have, if I wanted to rest,
The loveliest bed—just a nest
With soft, foamy billows beneath me
For pillows . . . if I were a tree
By the sea.

T. C. O'DONNELL.

## I'M GLAD

I'm glad the sky is painted blue,
And the earth is painted green,
With such a lot of nice fresh air
All sandwiched in between.

UNKNOWN.

## IN THE MORNING

When, in the morning, fresh from sleep,
I from my open window peep,
I always find some new surprise
To greet my grateful, wondering eyes.

I like to kneel and say my prayers
Before I hurry down the stairs—
Before the breakfast bell has gone—
And thank the Lord for all He's done.

While I was sleeping peacefully,
The Lord was working hard for me,
Making another lovely day
So I could stay outdoors and play.

Hundreds of daisies new and sweet
He's spread like stars around my feet.
And, knowing what I like the best,
He's put new birdlings in a nest.

Such heav'nly things He loves to do
For little folks like me and you.
I often wonder, while I play,
When does He take His holiday?

CECILIA LOFTUS.

## ISLANDS [1]

All the islands have run away
  From the land which is their mother;
Out where the lighthouse guards the bay
  They race with one another.

[1] *From "Pointed People." By permission of the Macmillan Co.*

Rocky or wooded, humped and small,
  Edged whitely round with spray,
What should we do if the islands all
  Ran back to land some day?

How would the ships know where to steer?
  Where would the sea-gulls fly?
How flat the sea would look, and queer,
  How lonely under the sky!

RACHEL LYMAN FIELD.

## JACK FROST

The door was shut, as doors should be,
  Before you went to bed last night;
Yet Jack Frost has got in, you see,
  And left your window silver white.

He must have waited till you slept;
  And not a single word he spoke,
But pencilled o'er the panes and crept
  Away again before you woke.

And now you cannot see the hills
  Nor fields that stretch beyond the lane;
But there are fairer things than these
  His fingers traced on every pane.

Rocks and castles towering high;
  Hills and dales, and streams and fields;
And knights in armor riding by,
  With nodding plumes and shining shields.

And here are little boats, and there
  Big ships with sails spread to the breeze;
And yonder, palm trees waving fair
  On islands set in silver seas.

And butterflies with gauzy wings;
  And herds of cows and flocks of sheep;
And fruits and flowers and all the things
  You see when you are sound asleep.

For, creeping softly underneath
  The door when all the lights are out,
Jack Frost takes every breath you breathe,
  And knows the things you think about.

He paints them on the window pane
  In fairy lines with frozen steam;
And when you wake you see again
  The lovely things you saw in dream.

GABRIEL SETOUN.

## JACK FROST

Jack Frost rapped on the window-pane
  And knocked on the door with his icicle cane.
"Excuse me," I said. "The door is shut tight,
  I'd rather you did not come in to-night."
So he wrote his name all over the glass
  And the baby sneezed as she heard him pass.

UNKNOWN.

## JACK FROST

When Jack Frost comes—oh! the fun.
  He plays his pranks on everyone.
He'll pinch your nose and bite your toes,
  But where he goes—nobody knows.

He paints upon the window-pane,
  Tin soldiers, teddy-bears and trains,
He nips the leaves from off the trees—
  This little man—nobody sees.

UNKNOWN.

## JACK FROST

Someone painted pictures on my
  Windowpane last night—
Willow trees with trailing boughs
  And flowers, frosty white,

And lovely crystal butterflies;
  But when the morning sun
Touched them with its golden beams,
  They vanished one by one!

HELEN BAYLEY DAVIS.

## LITTLE DAY MOON

The little day moon
Is a toy balloon
Lost by a child in its play:
It sailed so high
It stuck in the sky
And hangs there
At half-past noon.

NELLIE BURGET MILLER.

## LITTLE THINGS

Little drops of water,
  Little grains of sand,
Make the mighty ocean
  And the pleasant land.

E. C. BREWER.

## LITTLE WIND

Little Wind, blow on the hill top;
Little Wind, blow down the plain;
Little Wind, blow up the sunshine;
Little Wind, blow off the rain.

KATE GREENAWAY.

## LONELY WIND

I think the wind is curious,
To know the things we play
Around the fires at evening time,
And every stormy day.

He rattles at the latch and tries
To blow our curtains wide;
He pushes at the kitchen door
As though to come inside.

Poor Wind, we shut him out alone,
The livelong winter day,
And not a bird nor child's outside
With whom the Wind may play!

ELEANOR HAMMOND.

## MOON, SO ROUND AND YELLOW

Moon, so round and yellow,
Looking from on high,
How I love to see you
Shining in the sky.
Oft and oft I wonder,
When I see you there,
How they get to light you,

Hanging in the air!
Where you go at morning,
When the night is past,
And the sun comes peeping
O'er the hills at last.
Sometimes I will catch you
Slyly overhead,
When you think I'm sleeping
Snugly in my bed.

MATTHIAS BARR.

## MORNING CLOUDS

The long white clouds are Morning's wash,
Hung up in the sunny sky.
With work well done
Now she can run
And play till the clothes are dry.

NELLIE BURGET MILLER.

## MY FUNNY UMBRELLA

Oh, isn't it fun—when the rain comes down?
I like to go walking way down in the town.
The wind blows in gusts with all of its might,
And makes my umbrella dance—just like a kite!
It waves first to one side, and then back it flies—
To sail off without me, it certainly tries!

One day I had walked and was home—just about—
And my funny umbrella turned right inside out!

ALICE WILKINS.

## MY SHADOW

I have a little shadow that goes in and out with me,
And what can be the use of him is more than I can see.
He is very, very like me from the heels up to the head;
And I see him jump before me, when I jump into my bed.

The funniest thing about him is the way he likes to grow—
Not at all like proper children, which is always very slow;
For he sometimes shoots up taller like an india-rubber ball,
And he sometimes gets so little that there's none of him at all.

He hasn't got a notion of how children ought to play,
And can only make a fool of me in every sort of way.
He stays so close beside me, he's a coward you can see;
I'd think shame to stick to nursie as that shadow sticks to me!

One morning, very early, before the sun was up,
I rose and found the shining dew on every buttercup;
But my lazy little shadow, like an arrant sleepy-head,
Had stayed at home behind me and was fast asleep in bed.

ROBERT LOUIS STEVENSON.

## MY SWINGING SHADOW

In the morning when I swing,
It is the greatest fun,
To watch my shadow swinging high
With me in the sun.

Up he goes, and down he goes,
Then he kicks his heels,
Waves his hand and shakes his head,
So gay my shadow feels.

GRACE WILSON COPLEN.

## NATURE'S WASH DAY

Mother Nature had a wash day
And called upon the showers
To bathe the dusty faces
Of the little roadside flowers.
She scrubbed the green grass carpet
Until it shone like new.
She washed the faded dresses
Of the oaks and maples, too.
No shady nook or corner
Escaped her searching eye,
And then she sent the friendly sun
To shine and make them dry.

MARGUERITE GODE.

## NEIGHBORS

The newest moon is not so far
From a small and friendly evening star;
When day has gone and the sun is out,
What do you think they talk about?

Do they speak of the curious things of sky?
Of the time when a comet whistled by?
Or do they whisper across the air,
"Who is that little girl down there?"

ANNE BLACKWELL PAYNE.

## NOBODY KNOWS

Winds of the morning,
Bending the grasses,
Drinking the dewdrops,
Kissing the rose,

Where do you go
When the meadows are quiet
And sleepy at noontime?
Nobody knows.

Winds of the evening,
That dance in the tree-tops,
And sweep away clouds
From the moon till she glows,
Why don't you blow
Away the Old Sandman
That makes me so sleepy?
Nobody knows!

HELEN COALE CREW.

"North Wind, North Wind—oh, whither so fast?"
The answer whistled back on the blast:
"To yonder clouds I'm hurrying by,
To blow the snowflakes down from the sky."

UNKNOWN.

## PEBBLES

Pebbles, pebbles, pebbles,
For miles and miles and miles;
A sloping bank of pebbles
Round all the British Isles.

Grinding, grinding, grinding,
Where the billows pound,
Till they are smooth as marbles,
And often just as round.

White ones, grey ones, brown ones,
Lime and slate and quartz;
Yellow ones and pink ones,
Pebbles of all sorts.

Tinkle, tinkle, tinkle,
How strange it seems to think
That after all these ages
In my pail they clink.

Jewels, jewels, jewels,
For every child like me,
Oh, how I love the pebbles,
Beside the sounding sea!

EDITH KING.

## RAIN

I like to look out of my window and see
The rain dripping down on the leaves of a tree.

They shiver a little and bend in their places
While old Mother Nature is washing their faces.

HELEN WING.

## RAIN IN APRIL

Rain has such fun in April,
  It patters through the trees,
Talking to all the leaf buds
  And robins that it sees.

It splashes in the puddles
  And skips upon the walks,
Goes coasting down the grass blades
  And dandelion stalks.

It dips in all the flowers
  And when the clouds go by
It paints with flower colors
  A rainbow in the sky!

ELEANOR HAMMOND.

## RAIN IN THE CITY [1]

All the streets are a-shine with rain
The other side of my window pane.
Each motor car unrolls a track
Of red or green on the asphalt's black.
Beneath umbrellas people ply
Like giant toadstools stalking by.

RACHEL LYMAN FIELD.

## RAINBOWS

We watched the rain come pouring down,
Like tears from out the sky,
Until it seemed that all the world
Could never more be dry!

But while the trees were dripping still
And all the air was rain,
The sun broke through in rainbows
And the day was bright again!

And then my mother said, "Sweet child,
It's just the same with you—
Your eyes make rainbows of your tears
When smiles come breaking through!"

DIXIE WILLSON.

## RAINDROPS

I love to lie awake and hear
  The pitter-patter of the rain;
I make believe it plays with me,
  Tap-tapping on the windowpane!

[1] *From "Pointed People." By permission of the Macmillan Co.*

In daytime, too, I love to see
  The raindrops bounce upon the street;
They dance and skip like fairies gay,
  With crystal slippers on their feet.

ISLA P. RICHARDSON.

## RUBBER BOOTS

Little boots and big boots,
  Traveling together
On the shiny sidewalks,
  In the rainy weather,
Little boots and big boots,
  Oh, it must be fun
To splash the silver raindrops
  About you as you run,
Or scatter bits of rainbow
  Beneath the April sun!

Big boots and little boots,
  You know how it feels
To have the white clouds drifting
  Far below your heels;
And it is dizzy pleasure,
  Along the way to school,
To walk the lacy tree tops
  That lie in every pool.

Little boots and big boots,
  How you like to putter
In every slender streamlet
  That scampers down the gutter!

How you like to dabble
  Where the current crinkles
And fill the flowing water
  With new and wider wrinkles;

Or stir the yellow clay up
   To sudden, cloudy puffs
That dull the shining surface
   With muddy browns or buffs.

Big boots and little boots,
   Travel on together,
Merrily go splashing
   Through April's rainy weather!

ROWENA BASTIN BENNETT.

## RUNAWAY BROOK

"Stop, stop, pretty water!"
   Said Mary one day,
To a frolicsome brook
   That was running away.

"You run on so fast!
   I wish you would stay;
My boat and my flowers
   You will carry away.

"But I will run after:
   Mother says that I may;
For I would know where
   You are running away."

So Mary ran on;
   But I have heard say,
That she never could find
   Where the brook ran away.

ELIZA LEE FOLLEN.

## SHELL CASTLES

A sea shell is a castle
Where a million echoes roam,

A wee castle.
Sea castle,
Tossed up by the foam;
A wee creature's,
Sea creature's,
Long deserted home.

If I were very tiny,
I should walk those winding halls
And listen to the voices
In the pink and pearly walls;
And each mysterious echo
Would tell me salty tales
Of the phosphorescent fishes
And the white-winged ship that sails
On the sea's brim
Round the earth's rim
To the lilting of the gales;

Of the sea horse
That's a wee horse
And frolics in the sea
'Neath the coral
White and sorrel
That is the mermaid's tree;
And grazes on the seaweed
And the sea anemone;

But my ears cannot distinguish
The words it sings to me,
The sea shell,
The wee shell,
I hold so reverently,
And I only hear a whisper
Like the ghost voice of the sea.

ROWENA BASTIN BENNETT.

## SILVER[1]

Slowly, silently, now the moon
Walks the night in her silver shoon;
This way, and that, she peers, and sees
Silver fruit upon silver trees;
One by one the casements catch
Her beams beneath the silvery thatch;
Couched in his kennel, like a log,
With paws of silver sleeps the dog;
From their shadowy cote the white breasts peep
Of doves in silver-feathered sleep;
A harvest mouse goes scampering by,
With silver claws and silver eye;
And moveless fish in the water gleam,
By silver reeds in a silver stream.

WALTER DE LA MARE.

## SILVER SHEEP

The sun's a bright-haired shepherd boy,
Who drives the stars away;
Beyond the far blue meadows
He shuts them up by day.

At six or seven or eight o'clock,
Over the bars they leap—
The rams with horns of silver,
The little silver sheep.

And while the shepherd takes a nap
Behind a hill, near-by,
They roam the dusky pasture
And graze upon the sky.

ANNE BLACKWELL PAYNE.

[1] *From "Peacock Pie." By permission of Henry Holt & Co.*

## SNOW

The snow fell softly all the night.
It made a blanket soft and white.
It covered houses, flowers and ground,
But did not make a single sound!

ALICE WILKINS.

## SNOWMAN

One day we built a snowman
  We made him out of snow.
You'd ought to see how fine he was
  All white from top to toe.
We poured some water on him
  And froze him—legs and ears,
And when we went indoors to bed,
  I said he'd last two years.
But in the night, a warmer kind
  Of wind began to blow
And Winter cried and ran away,
  And with it ran the snow.
And in the morning when we went,
  To bid our friend, "Good day,"
There wasn't any snowman there,
  He'd melted all away.

UNKNOWN.

## SONG OF THE SNOWFLAKES [1]

We're very small, we're very small,
But we can cover the world and all;

[1] *Reprinted by permission from "For Days and Days." Copyright, 1919, by Frederick A. Stokes Co.*

We'll drop one by one in the middle of the night
And when you awake in the morning light,
You'll find not a stick or a stone in sight.

We're very small, we're very small.
You'll never hear us as we fall;
We'll cover the church, and we'll cover the tree,
And cover the people that come out to see
What a white, white world the world can be.

ANNETTE WYNNE.

## STARS

"I'm glad the stars are over me
And not beneath my feet,
Where we should trample on them
Like cobbles on the street.
I think it is a happy thing
That they are set so far;
It's best to have to look up high
When you would see a star."

UNKNOWN.

## STARS

A little boy sat dreaming
Upon his mother's lap,
That all the stars up in the sky
Fell down into his hat.

But when the dream was over,
What did the dreamer do?
Why, he looked into his hat,
And found it wasn't true.

UNKNOWN.

## SUNSET

When the sun has left the hilltop
  And the daisies' fringe is furled,
When the birds from wood and meadow
  In their hidden nests are curled,
Then I think of all the babies
  That are sleeping in the world.

There are babies in the high lands
  And babies in the low,
There are pale ones wrapped in furry skins
  On the margins of the snow,
And brown ones naked in the isles
  Where all the spices grow.

LAURENCE ALMA-TADEMA.

## TAKE CARE

Be still, Mr. Wind, be still!
For out on the top of the hill,
Where trailing arbutus and bluebells grow
And daisies swing and violets blow,
The fairies have brushed away the snow
  From everything
  And dance and sing
  In merry ring!

The Queen of the Fairies may
Let us come up to-day
On their fairy hill. And teach us to sing
Their Elfland songs; perhaps they'll bring
Their fairy babies for us to swing,
  For babies chill
  On top a hill
  Unless you're still.

And oh, Mr. Wind, do you know
Our Mothers say we may go
Back home with the fairies and see them parade
With the gnomes and the goblins 'way down in the glade
Where the tiniest children are never afraid—
So don't you dare
Give them a scare;
Mr. Wind, play fair!

ROSE WALDO.

## THE BROOK

I chatter over stony ways,
In little sharps and trebles,
I bubble into eddying bays,
I babble on the pebbles.

I chatter, chatter, as I flow
To join the brimming river,
For men may come and men may go,
But I go on forever.

I steal by lawns and grassy plots,
I slide by hazel covers;
I move the sweet forget-me-nots
That grow for happy lovers.

I slip, I slide, I gloom, I glance,
Among the skimming swallows;
I make the netted sunbeam dance
Against my sandy shallows.

And out again I curve and flow
To join the brimming river,
For men may come and men may go,
But I go on forever.

ALFRED TENNYSON.

## THE BROOK AND THE WILLOW TREE

Poor lonely willow tree
With nothing but the bubbling brook
To keep it company!

FROM THE JAPANESE.

## THE CLIFFTOP

The clifftop has a carpet
  Of lilac, gold and green.
The blue-sky bounds the ocean
  The white clouds scud between.

UNKNOWN.

## THE DEWDROPS

This morning before breakfast time
  Out in the garden there,
What do you think I really saw
  All over everywhere?

Among the grass and on the leaves,
  Shining on every tree!
Why, just the little twinkling stars,
  Come down to play with me!

My nursie wouldn't let me out
  Although I cried and cried.
She said I'd be all soaking wet,
  She'd never get me dried.

And when at last she let me go
  After the sun was high,
The pretty stars had all gone home
  Again into the sky!

LYDIA MILLER MACKAY

## THE FAN

Add but a handle
To the moon, and what a pretty
Fan it makes!

SOKAN (1456-1554)—JAPANESE.

## THE FIRST SNOWFALL[1]

The snow had begun in the gloaming,
And busily all the night
Had been heaping field and highway
With a silence deep and white.

Every pine and fir and hemlock
Wore ermine too dear for an earl,
And the poorest twig on the elm tree
Was ridged inch deep with pearl.

. . . . .

I stood and watched by the window
The noiseless work of the sky
And the sudden flurry of snow birds,
Like brown leaves whirling by.

JAMES R. LOWELL.

## THE GRASS

The grass so little has to do,
A sphere of simple green
With only butterflies to brood
And bees to entertain.

[1] *By permission of and arrangement with Houghton Mifflin Co.*

And stir all day to pretty tunes
The breezes fetch along
And hold the sunshine in its lap
And bow to everything.

EMILY DICKINSON.

## THE HILLS[1]

Sometimes I think the hills
That loom across the harbor
Lie there like sleeping dragons,
Crouched one above another,
With trees for tufts of fur
Growing all up and down
The ridges and humps of their backs,
And orange cliffs for claws
Dipped in the sea below.
Sometimes a wisp of smoke
Rises out of the hollows,
As if in their dragon sleep
They dreamed of strange old battles.

What if the hills should stir
Some day and stretch themselves,
Shake off the clinging trees
And all the clustered houses?

RACHEL LYMAN FIELD.

## THE MAN IN THE MOON

The Man in the Moon as he sails the sky
Is a very remarkable skipper.
But he made a mistake
When he tried to take
A drink of milk from the Dipper.

[1] *From "Pointed People." By permission of the Macmillan Co.*

He dipped right into the Milky Way
And slowly and carefully filled it.
The Big Bear growled
And the Little Bear howled,
And scared him so he spilled it.

UNKNOWN.

## THE MIST

The Mist is a soft white pussy-cat
That creeps so sly and still
Up from the willows by the brook
And crouches on the hill;
And then the sunshine runs away
To hide behind the mill—
For fear of this white creeping cat
The whole wide world is still.

NELLIE BURGET MILLER.

## THE MOON

The Moon is like a big round cheese
That shines above the garden trees,
And like a cheese grows less each night,
As though someone had had a bite.

The Mouse delights to nibble cheese,
The Dog bites anything he sees—
But how could they bite off the Moon?
Unless they went up in a balloon?

And Human People, when they eat
They think it rude to bite their meat,
They use a Knife or Fork or Spoon;
Who is it then that bites the Moon?

OLIVER HERFORD.

## THE MOON SHIP

In the ocean of the sky,
Borne on rising waves of cloud,
The moon ship
Goes a-gliding by
Through a forest of stars.

FROM THE JAPANESE.

## THE RAIN

"Open the window, and let me in,"
Sputters the merry rain;
"I want to splash down on the carpet, dear,
And I can't get through the pane.

"Here I've been tapping outside to you,
Why don't you come, if you're there?
The windows are shut or I'd dash right in,
And stream down the attic stair.

"I've washed the windows, I've spattered the blinds,
And that is not half what I've done;
I've bounced on the step and the side walk too
Till I've made the good people run."

UNKNOWN.

## RAIN

The rain is raining all around,
It falls on field and tree,
It rains on the umbrellas here,
And on the ships at sea.

ROBERT LOUIS STEVENSON.

## THE RAIN

The rain came down in torrents
And Mary said, "Oh! dear,
I'll have to wear my water proof,
And rubbers too, I fear."
So carefully protected—she started off for school
When the big round sun
Came out and chuckled—"April Fool."

UNKNOWN.

## THE RAINBOW[1]

Boats sail on the rivers,
And ships sail on the seas;
But clouds that sail across the sky
Are prettier far than these.

There are bridges on the rivers,
As pretty as you please;
But the bow that bridges heaven,
And overtops the trees,
And builds a road from earth to sky,
Is prettier far than these.

CHRISTINA ROSSETTI.

## THE SEA SHELL

Sea Shell, Sea Shell,
Sing me a song, O please!
A song of ships and sailor-men
Of parrots and tropical trees;

[1] *From "Sing Song." By permission of the Macmillan Co.*

Of islands lost in the Spanish Main
Which no man ever may see again,
Of fishes and corals under the waves,
And sea-horses stabled in great green caves—

Sea Shell, Sea Shell,
Sing of the things you know so well.

AMY LOWELL.

## THE SKY

I saw a shadow on the ground
And heard a bluejay going by;
A shadow went across the ground,
And I looked up and saw the sky.

It hung up on the poplar tree,
But while I looked it did not stay;
It gave a tiny sort of jerk
And moved a little bit away.

And farther on, and farther on
It moved, and never seemed to stop.
I think it must be tied with chairs,
And something pulls it from the top.

It never has come down again
And every time I look to see
The sky is always slipping back
And getting far away from me.

ELIZABETH MADOX ROBERTS.

## THE SUN'S TRAVELS

The sun is not a-bed, when I
At night upon my pillow lie;

Still round the earth his way he takes,
And morning after morning makes.

While here at home, in shining day,
We round the sunny garden play,
Each little Indian sleepy-head
Is being kissed and put to bed.

And when at eve I rise from tea,
Day dawns beyond the Atlantic Sea;
And all the children in the West
Are getting up and being dressed.

ROBERT LOUIS STEVENSON.

## THE TIDES

As once I played beside the sea,
Its waters gently came to me,
To bring me seaweed, stones, and shells,
And wash the sand where I dig wells.

But when I went another day,
The waters slowly flowed away,
To gather shells and pebbles more
For me to play with on the shore.

THOMAS TAPPER.

## THE TOP OF DAY

The sky is just the top of day;
Sometimes it's blue and sometimes gray;
And at the edges all around
The trees go up and it comes down.

ANNE BLACKWELL PAYNE.

## THE WIND [1]

Who has seen the wind?
  Neither I nor you;
But when the leaves hang trembling,
  The wind is passing through.

Who has seen the wind?
  Neither you nor I;
But when the trees bow down their heads,
  The wind is passing by.

CHRISTINA ROSSETTI.

## THE WIND

I saw you toss the kites on high
And blow the birds about the sky;
And all around I heard you pass,
Like ladies' skirts across the grass—
  O wind, a-blowing all day long,
  O wind, that sings so loud a song!

I saw the different things you did,
But always you yourself you hid.
I felt you push, I heard you call,
I could not see yourself at all—
  O wind, a-blowing all day long,
  O wind, that sings so loud a song!

O you that are so strong and cold,
O blower, are you young or old?
Are you a beast of field and tree,
Or just a stronger child than me?
  O wind, a-blowing all day long,
  O wind, that sings so loud a song!

ROBERT LOUIS STEVENSON.

[1] *From "Sing Song." By permission of the Macmillan Co.*

## THIRSTY FLOWERS

I have a little wat'ring pot,
  It holds a quart, I think,
And when the days are very hot
  I give the plants a drink.

They lift their heads as flowers should,
  And look so green and gay;
I'm sure that if they only could,
  "We thank you, Sir," they'd say.

ARTHUR A. KNIPE.

## TREE SHADOWS

All hushed the trees are waiting
On tiptoe for the sight
Of moonrise shedding splendor
Across the dusk of night.
Ah, now the moon is risen
And lo, without a sound
The trees all write their welcome
Far along the ground!

FROM THE JAPANESE.

## THE WONDERFUL WORLD

Great, wide, beautiful, wonderful World,
With the wonderful water round you curled,
And the wonderful grass upon your breast,—
World, you are beautifully dressed.

The wonderful air is over me,
And the wonderful wind is shaking the tree,
It walks on the water, and whirls the mills,
And talks to itself on the top of the hills.

You friendly earth! how far do you go
With the wheat fields that nod and the rivers that flow,
With cities and gardens, and cliffs, and isles
And people upon you for thousands of miles?

Ah! you are so great, and I am so small,
I tremble to think of you, World, at all;
And yet when I said my prayers, to-day,
A whisper inside me seemed to say,
"You are more than the Earth, though you are such
a dot;
You can love and think, and the Earth cannot!"

WILLIAM B. RANDS.

## TREE FEELINGS

I wonder if they like it—being trees?
I suppose they do. . . .
It must feel good to have the ground so flat,
And feel yourself stand straight up like that—
So stiff in the middle—and then branch at ease,
Big boughs that arch, small ones that bend and blow,
And all those fringy leaves that flutter so.
You'd think they'd break off at the lower end
When the wind fills them, and their great heads bend.
But then you think of all the roots they drop,
As much at bottom as there is on top,—
A double tree, widespread in earth and air
Like a reflection in the water there.

I guess they like to stand still in the sun
And just breathe out and in, and feel the cool sap run
And like to feel the rain run through their hair
And slide down to the roots and settle there.
But I think they like the wind best. From the light
touch
That lets the leaves whisper and kiss so much,

To the great swinging, tossing, flying wide,
And all the time so stiff and strong inside!
And the big Winds, that pull, and make them feel
How long their roots are, and the earth how leal!
And O the blossoms! And the wild seeds lost!
And jewelled martyrdom of fiery frost!
And fruit trees. I'd forgotten. No cold gem,
But to apples—and bow down with them!

HARLOTTE PERKINS STETSON.

## TREES USED IN GAMES AND SPORTS

Think of all the games you play,
Baseball, tennis, and croquet,
Checkers, chess, and dominoes,
Games that everybody knows.

And the fun you have in school,
In the gym and in the pool,
Racing round the running track,
Jumping from the springboard's back.

Think of summer sports and fun,
Fishing, hunting with a gun,
Climbing trees, and paddling, too,
In a rowboat or canoe.

Games and good times by the score,
Those we've named and many more,
Each and every one of these
Depends on wood that comes from trees.

MARY I. CURTIS.

## TWINKLE, TWINKLE, LITTLE STAR

Twinkle, twinkle, little star,
How I wonder what you are!
Up above the world so high,
Like a diamond in the sky.

When the blazing sun is gone,
When he nothing shines upon,
Then you show your little light,
Twinkle, twinkle, all the night.

In the dark blue sky you keep,
And often through my curtains peep,
For you never shut an eye
Till the sun is in the sky.

As your bright and tiny spark
Lights the traveler in the dark,
Though I know not what you are,
Twinkle, twinkle, little star.

JANE TAYLOR.

## VERY LOVELY

Wouldn't it be lovely if the rain came down
Till the water was quite high over all the town?
If the cabs and buses all were set afloat,
And we had to go to school in a little boat?

Wouldn't it be lovely if it still should pour
And we all went up to live on the second floor?
If we saw the butcher sailing up the hill,
And we took the letters in at the window sill?

It's been raining, raining, all the afternoon;
All these things might happen really very soon.
If we woke to-morrow and found they had begun,
Wouldn't it be glorious? *Wouldn't* it be fun?

ROSE FYLEMAN.

## WASHDAY

Mrs. Ocean takes in washing
Every day the whole year through
And she uses so much bluing
That it stains the water blue.
I have seen soap suds floating
When the waves were rough and high,
But I never have discovered
Where she hangs the clothes to dry.

ELIZABETH F. UPSON.

## WATER NOISES

When I am playing by myself,
And all the boys are lost around,
Then I can hear the water go—
It makes a little talking sound.

Along the rocks below the tree,
I see it ripple up and wink;
And I can hear it saying on,
"And do you think? And do you think?"

A bug shoots by that snaps and ticks,
And a bird flies up beside the tree
To go into the sky to sing.
I hear it say, "Killdee, Killdee!"

Or else a yellow cow comes down
To splash a while and have a drink

But when she goes I still can hear
The water say, "And do you think?"

ELIZABETH MADOX ROBERTS.

## WHEN WE PLANT A TREE

What do we plant when we plant a tree?
We plant a home that is to be—
A ship to sail across the sea—
A desk, a chair, a book maybe—
These we plant when we plant a tree.

What do we plant when we plant a tree?
Beauty and joy for all to see—
A home for birds to bide a wee—
Grateful shade for you and me—
These we plant when we plant a tree.

WARREN P. LANDERS.

## WHO LIKES THE RAIN?

"I," said the duck, "I call it fun,
For I have my little red rubbers on;
They make a cunning three-toed track
In the soft, cool mud. Quack! Quack! Quack!"

"I," cried the dandelion, "I.
My roots are thirsty, my buds are dry":
And she lifted a towsled yellow head
Out of her green and grassy bed.

"I hope 'twill pour! I hope 'twill pour!"
Purred the tree toad at his gray back door,
"For, with a broad leaf for a roof,
I am perfectly weatherproof."

Sang the brook: "I laugh at every drop,
And wish they never need to stop
Till a big, big river I grew to be,
And could find my way out to the sea."

"I," shouted Ted, "for I can run,
With my high-top boots and my rain coat on,
Through every puddle and runlet and pool
That I find on my way to school."

CLARA DOTY BATES.

## WIND SONG

Here comes the wind, with a noise and a whirr,
Out on the streets he is making a stir.
Now he sends flying a fine, stiff hat,
Tosses and leaves it all muddy and flat;
Turns an umbrella quite inside out,
Tears up stray papers and scatters about,
Makes big balloons out of ladies' long capes,
Skirts into sails, then—the queerest of shapes.
The wind is an enemy, often we say:
"We never quite like it—a windy day!"

The wind blows the seeds from their close little pods
And scatters them far away—rods upon rods;
He plants them where never an eye could see
Place for their growing and blooming to be.
He blows away rain, and scatters the dew,
He sweeps the earth clean and makes it all new.
He blows away sickness and brings good health
He comes overladen with beauty and wealth.
Oh, the wind is a friend! Let us always say:
"We love it! We love it!—a windy day!"

UNKNOWN.

## A LITTLE GIRL IN BLOOM

There is the quaintest little girl—
A small, sweet Japanese,
Who lives within a paper house
Beside the cherry trees,
And she has hair that's dark and straight,
Black eyes that slant and shine
And skin that's very soft and smooth,
But not so white as mine.

Her dress is like a garden gay
That reaches to her toes,
All sprinkled with chrysanthemums
Of dainty blue and rose.
A silken sash around her waist,
The color of the sky,
Spreads out across her shoulders slim
Just like a butterfly.

Her clogs are just as tiny quite
As Cinderella's shoe,
For great big girls like you and me
I'm sure they'd never do.
Her flowing sleeves are very strange,
So long and deep and wide,
That I should think her slender arms
Would both get lost inside.

I wish this little girl in bloom,
Would leave her cherry tree,
And leave her little paper house
And come and visit me,
And tell me of the songs she sings,
The games she likes to play,
But I am afraid she never will,
She lives so far away.

ANNE BLACKWELL PAYNE.

## CHAIRS[1]

Indian children squat upon the ground.
Their parents have no chairs around;
They have no chairs, but never mind,
For squatting is all right, they find.

ANNETTE WYNNE.

## FOREIGN CHILDREN

Little Indian, Sioux or Crow,
Little frosty Eskimo,
Little Turk or Japanee,
O! don't you wish that you were me?

You have seen the scarlet trees
And the lions over seas;
You have eaten ostrich eggs,
And turned the turtles off their legs.

Such a life is very fine,
But it's not so nice as mine:
You must often, as you trod,
Have wearied *not* to be abroad.

You have curious things to eat,
I am fed on proper meat;
You must dwell beyond the foam,
But I am safe and live at home.

Little Indian, Sioux or Crow,
Little frosty Eskimo,
Little Turk or Japanee,
O! don't you wish that you were me?

ROBERT LOUIS STEVENSON.

[1] *Reprinted by permission from "For Days and Days." Copyright, 1919, by Frederick A. Stokes Co.*

## HIAWATHA'S CHILDHOOD

(Selections)

By the shores of Gitche Gumee,
By the shining Big-Sea-Water,
Stood the wigwam of Nokomis
Daughter of the Moon, Nokomis.
Dark behind it rose the forest,
Rose the black and gloomy pine-trees,
Rose the firs with cones upon them;
Bright before it beat the water,
Beat the clear and sunny water,
Beat the shining Big-Sea-Water.
There the wrinkled old Nokomis
Nursed the little Hiawatha,
Rocked him in his linden cradle,
Bedded soft in moss and rushes,
Safely bound with reindeer sinews;
Stilled his fretful wail by saying:
"Hush! the Naked Bear will hear thee!"
Lulled him into slumber, singing:
"Ewa-yea! my little owlet!
Who is this that lights the wigwam?
With his great eyes lights the wigwam?
Ewa-yea! my little owlet!"
Many things Nokomis taught him
Of the stars that shine in heaven;
Showed him Ishkoodah, the comet,
Ishkoodah, with fiery tresses;
At the door on Summer evenings
Sat the little Hiawatha;
Heard the whispering of the pine-trees,
Heard the lapping of the waters,
Sounds of music, words of wonder;
"Minne-wawa!" said the pine-trees.
"Mudway-aushka!" said the water.

Saw the firefly, Wah-wah-taysee,
Flitting through the dusk of evening,
With the twinkle of its candle
Lighting up the brakes and bushes,
And he sang the song of children,
Sang the song Nokomis taught him:
"Wah-wah-taysee, little fire-fly,
Little, flitting, white-fire insect,
Little, dancing, white-fire creature,
Light me with your little candle,
Ere upon my bed I lay me,
Ere in sleep I close my eyelids!"
Saw the moon rise from the water,
Rippling, rounding from the water,
Saw the flecks and shadows on it,
Whispered: "What is that, Nokomis?"
And the good Nokomis answered:
"Once a warrior, very angry,
Seized his grandmother, and threw her
Up into the sky at midnight;
Right against the moon he threw her:
'Tis her body that you see there."
Saw the rainbow in the heaven,
In the eastern sky, the rainbow,
Whispered, "What is that, Nokomis?"
And the good Nokomis answered:
"'Tis the heaven of flowers you see there;
All the wild-flowers of the forest,
All the lilies of the prairie,
When on earth they fade and perish,
Blossom in that heaven above us."
When he heard the owls at midnight,
Hooting, laughing in the forest,
"What is that?" he cried in terror;
"What is that?" he said, "Nokomis?"
And the good Nokomis answered:
"That is but the owl and owlet,
Talking in their native language,
Talking, scolding at each other."

Then the little Hiawatha
Learned of every bird its language,
Learned their names and all their secrets,
How they build their nests in Summer,
Where they hide themselves in Winter,
Talked with them whene'er he met them,
Called them "Hiawatha's Chickens."
Of all beasts he learned the language,
Learned their names and all their secrets,
How the beavers built their lodges,
Where the squirrels hid their acorns,
How the reindeer ran so swiftly,
Why the rabbit was so timid,
Talked with them whene'er he met them,
Called them "Hiawatha's Brothers."

HENRY W. LONGFELLOW.

## INDIAN CHILDREN[1]

Where we walk to school each day,
Indian children used to play—
All about our native land,
Where the shops and houses stand.

And the trees were very tall,
And there were no streets at all,
Not a church and not a steeple—
Only woods and Indian people.

Only wigwams on the ground,
And at night bears prowling round—
What a different place today
Where we live and work and play!

ANNETTE WYNNE.

[1] *Reprinted by permission from "For Days and Days." Copyright, 1919, by Frederick A. Stokes Co.*

## NEIGHBORS

Sometimes my brother lets me look
In his Geography;
The lands are painted rainbow bright;
The blue is for the sea,
And in each foreign country there are
Children just like me.

Of course their clothes are not like mine;
Their hair is different too;
At dinner time they never eat
The kind of food I do,
And playtime *here* is bedtime *there.*
(My brother says it's true.)

But they are happy just the same
'Cause each one has a mother,
And I suppose they mostly have
A sister and a brother;
I think it would be lots of fun
If we could know each other.

That's why I'm going to build a boat
And sail it by a star,
Until it bumps against the shore
Where all these children are.
(I looked in the Geography;
It isn't very far!)

HELEN WING.

## OTHER CHILDREN

Some children live in palaces
Behind an iron gate
And go to sleep in beds of gold
Whenever it gets late.

Some other children live in tents
With feathers all around
And take their naps in blankets
That are spread upon the ground.

And way up north the children live
In houses built of ice
And think that beds made out of fur
Are really very nice.

In countries where the nights are hot,
Without a single breeze,
The children sleep on bamboo beds
That fasten in the trees.

Some day I think I'll travel 'round
And visit every land
And learn to speak the language that
Each child can understand.

They'll teach me how to play their games
And, if they want me to,
I'll show them diff'rent kinds of tricks
That I know how to do.

They'll want to ask me questions then
And I will ask them others,
Until at last we understand
Like sisters and like brothers.

HELEN WING.

## QUEER HABITS

An Eskimo baby, all dressed up in fur,
Who lives in a little igloo,
Must warm up his toes by a fire made of moss,
Now, doesn't this seem queer to you?

And when he is good, as most Eskimos are,
  His mother brings out a raw fish,
And gives him a mouthful to have for dessert,
  Now doesn't this seem a queer dish?

No doubt if this Eskimo baby came down
  From far snowy lands, it would seem
Even queerer to him, that we eat with such glee
  A big chilly mound of ice cream!

CORNEILLE MCCARN.

## THE LITTLE TOY LAND OF THE DUTCH

Away, 'way off 'cross the seas and such
Lies the little flat land of the Dutch, Dutch, Dutch!

Where the green toy meadows stretch off to the sea,
With a little canal where the fence ought to be.

Where the windmills' arms go round, round, round,
And sing to the cows with a creaky sound.

Where storks live up in the chimney top,
And the wooden shoes go plop, plop, plop!

Where little toy houses stand in a row,
And dog carts clattering past them go!

Where milk cans shine in the shiniest way,
And the housemaids scrub, scrub, scrub all day.

Where dykes keep out the raging sea,
And shut in the land as cosy as can be.

Oh, that little toy land, I like it much,
That prim little, trim little, land of the Dutch.

ANON.

## AFTERWARDS[1]

When the "Our Father" I have said,
And Mother tucks me into bed,
And kisses me, and calls "Good night!
God bless you!" and turns out the light,

Why, then I lie awake and say
Another prayer a different way.
I talk to God, and angels keep
Their wings around me till I sleep.

I talk to God, and tell Him things
All in between the angels' wings,
And God leans down, and says "I know!
I understand! I love you so!"

MARY DIXON THAYER.

## CHRISTMAS "GOOD NIGHT"

Was Jesus just a boy like me
And did He have a Christmas tree?

And was His star the brightest star?
And could you see it very far?

And were the Shepherds good, kind men?
And did they have a dog like Ben,

That stayed and watched the little sheep,
When they found Jesus, fast asleep?

And were the Wisemen very wise?
And did the light blind both their eyes?

[1] *From "A Child on His Knees." By permission of the Macmillan Co.*

Was Mary glad it was a boy,
And not a girl like Baby Joy?

And did the Father know the way
That little children like to play?

And did three cousins stay for tea?
Think He would come and play with me?

And was His Uncle Will like mine?
And did they have a lovely time?

And did it snow, or was it bright?
I'll go to sleep . . . Good-night . . . Good-
night.

ETHEL ROBB.

## HOW NICE [1]

How nice it is, dear God, to know
That You made all the flowers grow!

How nice it is to stop and think
You made the spring from which I drink!

How nice it is to know that You
Painted the sky that lovely blue!

How nice it is to know You fill
The night with stars and always will!

But oh, how nice to know You made
Me too! Sometimes I am afraid

I do not thank You as I should—
You are so wise, dear God, and good!

MARY DIXON THAYER.

[1] *From "A Child on His Knees." By permission of the Macmillan Co.*

## RIDDLES

The answers to all riddles will be found on page 315 under Riddles in the "Index to Interest."

I

First it was a pretty flower, dressed in pink and white,
Then it was a tiny ball, almost hid from sight.
Round and green and large it grew—then it turned to red.
It will make a splendid pie for your Thanksgiving Spread.

UNKNOWN.

2

My castle has a lot of doors;
Each one is numbered too.
No matter which you open first,
Two pages wait on you.

L. J. BRIDGMAN.

3

I tied him tight with a good stout twine,
One end unto the other,
Then, when I pulled the string, he kicked
And off flew his slim brother.

L. J. BRIDGMAN.

4

There's a flower in the garden,
It's just like a cup;
It's yellow, as yellow as butter,
And they call it ——

UNKNOWN.

5

To squeeze through little narrow slits,
Is what they have to do,

And holes are made in peoples clothes
To let them peek-a-boo!

L. J. BRIDGMAN.

6

Little Nancy Etticoat,
In a white petticoat,
  With a red nose!
The longer she stands,
The shorter she grows.

NURSERY RHYME.

7

He used to crawl along the ground,
Then busy spinning he was found,
He hung his cradle on a bough,
And, in it, he is sleeping now.

UNKNOWN.

8

Although he has a splendid back,
  He hasn't any head,
And though his arms are very strong,
  He never has been fed.

His legs are strong, yet never have
  I seen him run and play.
You sit upon his lap, I think,
  For hours every day.

L. J. BRIDGMAN.

9

Red within and black without,
With four corners round about.

OLD RHYME.

10

As round as a biscuit
As busy as a bee;
The prettiest little thing
That you ever did see!

UNKNOWN.

11

Hands without fingers and feet without toes;
A round white face, but never a nose,
With hands that travel while feet repose,
Standing still it always goes.

With neither mouth, nor throat, nor tongue,
Its voice persists the whole day long,
For should it cease its tuneless song
Why, then our times would all go wrong!

H. S. BENNETT.

12

Like a bird it softly flies
Through the soft October skies.

UNKNOWN.

13

Black we are, but much admired.
Men seek for us till they are tired.
We tire horse, but comfort man.
Tell me this riddle, if you can.

UNKNOWN.

14

I am as black as black can be, but yet I shine,
My home was deep within the earth, in a dark mine.
Though black I seem to be, yet I can glow;
Just put me on a blazing fire, and you will know.

UNKNOWN.

15

I'm a pretty little thing,
   Always coming in the Spring.
In the meadows I am found,
   Peeping just above the ground.
And my stalk is covered flat,
   With a white and yellow hat.

UNKNOWN.

16

'Tis a gay sort of lion
All dressed green and yellow.
I've pulled the head off
Of many a fellow.

He stands in the grass,
But he never prowls 'round;
When I blow off his hair
He makes never a sound.

L. J. BRIDGMAN.

17

A million little diamonds sparkling on the trees,
And all the children said: "A jewel if you please!"
But when they stood with hands outstretched
      To catch the jewels gay,
A million little sunbeams came and took them all away.

UNKNOWN.

18

In marble walls as white as milk,
Lined with a skin as soft as silk;
Within a fountain crystal clear,
A golden apple doth appear.
No doors there are to this stronghold,
Yet thieves break in and steal the gold.

OLD RHYME.

19

He likes his bath so very well
  He eats his dinner in it.
I say, "Come out and take a walk."
  He won't come for a minute!

I dropped a line to him, one day,
  Invited him to travel,
And when he came he wouldn't walk
  But lay upon the gravel.

L. J. BRIDGMAN.

20

Riddle me, riddle me, what is that,
Over the head, and under the hat?

UNKNOWN.

21

Somebody's been in the garden
  Nipping the blossoms fair;
All the green leaves are blackened;
  Who do you think was there?

UNKNOWN.

22

His coat of steel is shining bright,
  Yet Mr. K. is not a knight.
He keeps our foes outside our door,—
  His height in inches seldom four!

Inside a hole his head I popped;
  A twist, and lo! a man was stopped!
A big strong man was stopped, I say,
  And all by little Mr. K.

L. J. BRIDGMAN.

23

First they dress in green,
  Then they change this gown,
And each one is seen,
  Red, or gold, or brown.

UNKNOWN.

24

First they danced upon the trees,
Then they floated on the breeze,
Then they gaily blew around—
Now they're sleeping on the ground.

UNKNOWN.

25

There is one that has a head without an eye,
And there's one that has an eye without a head:
You may find the answer if you try;
And when all is said
Half the answer hangs upon a thread!

CHRISTINA ROSSETTI.

*From "Sing Song." By permission of the Macmillan Co.*

26

Old Mother Twitchet had but one eye,
And a long tail that she let fly;
And every time she went through a gap,
A bit of her tail she left in the trap.

OLD RHYME.

27

A tiny baby dressed in green,
Sits in a cradle brown.
At first high in the air, it's seen,
And then it tumbles down.

UNKNOWN.

28

A little brown baby, round and wee,
With the kind wind to rock him, slept high in a tree;
And he grew, and he grew, till, oh dreadful to say!
He tumbled right out of his cradle one day.
Down, down from the tree-top, a terrible fall!
But the queer little fellow was not hurt at all!
And sound and sweet he lies in the grass
And there you will find him whenever you pass.

UNKNOWN.

29

A few still patter, as they fall,
The squirrels did not get them all.

UNKNOWN.

30

Two brown babies in a rough green ball,
Swinging away in the tree-top tall
Up came the wind and blew a hard blast
Green prickly ball hold fast! hold fast!
Down to the ground with an awful thump
Fell the green ball—and such a hard bump
Cracked it wide and the brownies jumped out—
The boys picked them up with many a shout.

UNKNOWN.

31

Little yellow twins were they,
Both neatly dressed in red.
I broke into their yellow house
And took them from their bed.

I think you've done the very same;
So don't complain of me.
You've swallowed many just such twins
Now, guess what they can be.

L. J. BRIDGMAN.

32

Hard and yellow,
See the fellow,
As he dances,
Jumps and prances,
Snaps his jacket,
Hear him crack it!
Now he's whiter,
Softer, lighter.

L. J. BRIDGMAN.

34

They every one have eyes, but not one of them can see,
You find them every size. They are good as they can be.
You can dig them in a field, in a hill they hide away.
You will eat them just at noon, almost any day!

UNKNOWN.

35

It will make a jack-o'-lantern or a big
Thanksgiving pie,
It's a big round yellow something, you can
guess it if you try.

UNKNOWN.

36

"Pussy, pussy, come to me!"
Pussy stuck fast to her tree,
So I took tree, puss and all,
Stuck them up upon the wall.

L. J. BRIDGMAN.

37

You can hear me singing merrily,
Most any morning early,
For I am hunting through the fields,
For wild buckwheat and barley.
Just whistle to me once or twice.
I may not come in view,
But I will answer sweet and clear
"Bob-Bob White!—back at you.

MARION MITCHELL WALKER.

38

Who am I?
I come from the sky;
I wash the grass,
And over the road
You may hear me pass

The flowers all love me
So do the trees—
I make the brooks sing
As they run to the seas.

UNKNOWN.

39

It's a brother to the hatchet,
  And a cousin to the knife.
It has many teeth, but never
  Swallowed once in all its life.

The carpenter was looking
  And I said, "Do you see it gnaw!"
He answered, "Yes, I noticed,
  I observed, in fact I saw."

L. J. BRIDGMAN.

40

We're a jolly pair of twins, and we always work together.
We are always bright and sharp, however dull the weather,
Whenever little Mary takes her workbox in her lap
We are always up and ready with our snip, snap, snap.

We cut the dolly's mantle; we shape the baby's dress,
Oh! half the clever things we do, you'd never, never guess.
For food or sleep or playtime, we do not care a rap,
But we're always up and ready with our snip, snap, snap.

UNKNOWN.

42

Thirty white horses
  Upon a red hill,
Now they tramp,
Now they champ,
  Now they stand still.

NURSERY RHYME.

43

Ten little servants, and
Five go together.
When they walk out, they are
All dressed in leather.

Five in one overcoat,
Five in another,
Each little chap has a
Little twin brother.

L. J. BRIDGMAN.

44

Miss Topsy Turvy will not go
Unless she's dressed precisely so!
Go dress her in a suit of twine
And then she'll dance about quite fine.

L. J. BRIDGMAN.

45

Ribbons, strings,
Pretty things,
To guess my name you're trying.
O'er the snow,
The mailman goes;
With him I'll be flying.

In a row
Hearts will show
All the love I'm sending.
Scallops, lace,
Each in place,—
Love and beauty blending.

Arrows dart
Through each heart,
Thus my true love showing.

Guess once more
For to your door
  I will soon be going.

DORA MON DORE.

46

As soft as silk, as white as milk,
As bitter as gall, a thick green wall,
And a green coat covers me all.

UNKNOWN.

47

It roared and ran and disappeared
Its brothers tumbled after
It made me turn a somersault,
At which there was much laughter.

It often wears a soft white cap
When winds are loudly wailing,
And sailors find its relatives
Where any ship is sailing.

L. J. BRIDGMAN.

48

Riddle-me, riddle-me, riddle-me-ree,
Perhaps you can tell what this riddle may be!
As deep as a house, as round as a cup,
And all the King's horses can't draw it up.

NURSERY RHYME.

49

He puffs and puffs the tugging kites
  Until they sail so high
They look like tiny flying birds
  Against the arching sky.

UNKNOWN.

50

It made a rustling sound
As softly through the leaves it blew,
But now it roughly swirls around
And seems to say: "Boo-oo."

UNKNOWN.

51

A gay little bird in a jaunty red cap.
With busy black beak that goes rap-a-tap;
I build my house quickly, and neatly, 'tis said;
But please, oh please, do not call me
"Red Head!"

MARION MITCHELL WALKER.

## A MAY BASKET

A robin has flown away up in the tree!
And what do you think he has hung there for me?
A basket of birdies, all fluffy and wee,
For it's May Day! It's May Day! It's May Day, you see!

LILIAN BAYNE WEST.

A pretty brook was running at play
With little Jack Frost on a cold winter's day.
It stopped to rest at the foot of a hill
Making a pond all quiet and still.
"Aha!" said Jack Frost, "Now isn't this nice?"
And quickly he turned the water to ice.

UNKNOWN.

## A SLEIGH-RIDE

Ting! ring! the sleigh bells jingle
Merrily over the frozen snow.
Cheeks a-glow and ears a-tingle,
Tumble in, children, here we go!

Ting! ring! the sleigh-bells jingle!
  Get along, Dobbin! go along, Jack!
Bells and voices merrily mingle,
  Swift we fly as an arrow's track.

Ting! ring! the sleigh-bells jingle!
  Nose cold, Tommy? Here, rub it with snow!
Toes ache, Ned? Just kick till they tingle,
  Thump! thump! thump! on the dasher, so!

Ting! ring! the sleigh-bells jingle!
  Snow-wreaths fly like a snow-sea's foam.
Sweet bells, sweet laugh, hark! how they mingle!
  Tumble out, children, here we're at home!

LAURA E. RICHARDS.

## APRIL [1]

The roofs are shining from the rain
The sparrows twitter as they fly,
And with a windy April grace
The little clouds go by.

Yet the back-yards are bare and brown
With only one unchanging tree.
I could not be so sure of spring
Save that it sings in me.

SARA TEASDALE.

## AUTUMN

The trees are all wonderful yellow and red
  And the nuts fall down on the ground.
The children go shuffling through the leaves,
  They like the rustling sound.

[1] *From "Rivers to the Sea." By permission of the Macmillan Co.*

The squirrels hide their winter's store
And then come out to look for more.

ARTHUR A. KNIPE.

## AUTUMN FIRES

In the other gardens
And all up the vale,
From the autumn bonfires
See the smoke trail!

Pleasant summer over
And all the summer flowers,
The red fire blazes,
The gray smoke towers.

Sing a song of seasons!
Something bright in all!
Flowers in the summer,
Fires in the fall!

ROBERT LOUIS STEVENSON.

## AUTUMN GLOVES

Through the frosty air to the woods we go
In search of walnuts sweet,
We pick up balls, some of green, some brown,
We shake the trees and more tumble down
In a shower, at our feet!

Hauling home our horde, then we hull them out—
These goodies, ev'ry one loves,
And now we lay them in the sun to dry
And find no matter how we try
We can't wash off our gloves!

MILDRED D. SHACKLETT.

## AUTUMN RACES

When leaves are dressed in red and brown,
And racing through the air,
Then all the children of our town,
Run races everywhere.
The wind is blowing high and free,
The sun is smiling, too,—
When brother calls his dog and me,
He knows what he will do.

We three go racing down the lane—
Then Rover makes a fuss,
Until we run back home again,
Where Mother waits for us.
If Daddy meets us at the gate,
We race him to the door,
Then Mother calls, "It is too late
To play out any more."

White clouds run races in the sky,
While we must stay below;
When clouds are quickly passing by,
We wonder where they go.
It must be such a jolly place,
To live in skies of blue,
Where all the day the clouds may race,
With airplanes flying through.

EMILIE BLACKMORE STAPP.

## AUTUMN TRAIN

Autumn is a train that travels
From Summerland to Winterville—
Mellow apples, yellow pumpkins
And sweet brown nuts its freight cars fill;

Flying fast its hot breath changes
The green of leaves to red and gold,
And when it pulls up at the station
Then children know 'twill soon grow cold.

MILDRED D. SHACKLETT.

## BED IN SUMMER

In winter I get up at night
And dress by yellow candle-light.
In summer, quite the other way,
I have to go to bed by day.

I have to go to bed and see
The birds still hopping on the tree,
Or hear the grown-up people's feet
Still going past me in the street.

And does it not seem hard to you,
When all the sky is clear and blue,
And I should like so much to play,
To have to go to bed by day?

ROBERT LOUIS STEVENSON.

## BELONGING TO SUMMER

Summer is full of things that are good,
Wading in the brook and tramping in the wood;
Climbing the trees and shaking down cherries;
Swinging a pail and picking blackberries;
Smelling the hay and doing the chores;
Packing a kit and cooking outdoors;
Playing croquet with ball and with mallet
And sleeping, when comp'ny comes, down on a pallet!

MILDRED D. SHACKLETT.

## FOUR KINDS OF WADING

We go wading in the winter
When the clouds are hanging low
With our feet in stout galoshes
Through the drifts of fleecy snow!

We go wading in the springtime
With our happy, twinkling feet
Dressed in new and shiny slippers
Through the clover red and sweet!

We go wading in the summer
In a shady, pebbly pool
With our feet so white and naked
Through the water fresh and cool!

We go wading in the autumn
In a frosty, tingling breeze
With our feet in dusty oxfords
Through the piles of rustling leaves!

MILDRED D. SHACKLETT.

## CATKIN

I have a little pussy,
  And her coat is silver grey;
She lives in a great wide meadow
  And she never runs away.
She always is a pussy,
  She'll never be a cat
Because—she's a pussy willow!
  Now what do you think of that!

UNKNOWN.

## ICE

When it is the winter time
I run up the street
And I make the ice laugh
With my little feet—
"Crickle, crackle, crickle
Crrreeet, crrreeet, crrreeet."

DOROTHY ALDIS.

I had a little snowball once
It was so round and white;
I took it home with me
And tried to keep it overnight;
But when next morning I awoke,
Just at the break of day,
I went to get it—and I found
It had melted all away!

UNKNOWN.

## KEEPING STORE

We have bags and bags of whitest down
Out of the milkweed pods;
We have purple asters in lovely heaps,
And stacks of golden-rods.

We have needles out of sweet pine woods,
And spools of cobweb thread;
We have bachelors' buttons for dolly's dress,
And hollyhock caps for her head.

MARY F. BUTTS.

## LEARNING TO SWIM

I'm learning how to dive and swim;
The lake is awfully cool and dim,

It's bigger than I've ever seen,
And all the water looks real green.

Of course I'm trying very hard;
The other day I swam a yard,

And my chum shouted, "good" at me,
And said, "Now keep it up, Bob Lee!"

And I began to think about,—
The time when I can be a scout!

ANNA MEDARY.

## LITTLE JACK FROST

Little Jack Frost went up the hill,
Watching the stars and moon so still,
Watching the stars and moon so bright,
And laughing aloud with all his might.

Little Jack Frost ran down the hill,
Late in the night when the winds were still,
Late in the fall when the leaves fell down,
Red and yellow and faded brown.

Little Jack Frost walked through the trees,
"Oh!" sighed the flowers, "we freeze, we freeze,"
"Oh," sighed the grasses, "we die, we die."
Said Little Jack Frost, "Good-by, good-by."

Little Jack Frost went round and round,
Spreading white snow on the frozen ground,

Nipping the breezes, icing the streams,
And chilling the warmth of the sun's bright beams.

But when Dame Nature brought back the spring,
Brought back the birds to chirp and sing,
Melted the snow and warmed the sky,
Then Little Jack Frost went pouting by.

The flowers opened their eyes of blue,
Green buds peeped out and grasses grew;
It was so warm and scorched him so,
That Little Jack Frost was glad to go.

UNKNOWN.

## LITTLE SPRING

She lies in her little bed
With the coverlet up to her chin—
"Dear me," she thinks, "I should like to get up
If I only knew where to begin."
But she is too drowsy to lift her head,
And her feet are fastened in.
She sees through the curtain's chinks
That the sky is getting blue,
And there is a sound like a bluebird's note—
She has nothing else to do
So she picks a hole in the coverlet
And pushes her fingers through.
How she laughs to see them there
All sticking up in a row!
They beckon the birds and breezes soft—
Do you wonder how I know?
I saw them out in the crocus bed—
Not very long ago.

UNKNOWN.

## MARCH

March is a worker, busy and merry,
  Driving the clouds away,
Herding them down the lanes of the sky,
  Whistling as though it were play,

Shoveling the snow away from the valleys,
  Clearing the gardens and hills,
Calling the daffodils, shaking the maples,
  Waking the brooklets and rills.

All the day long he never stops whistling,
  He's the merriest month of the year!
Hear him go shouting down highways and byways,
  "Get to work! Springtime is here!"

ELEANOR HAMMOND.

## MARCH WIND

The wind is pushing against the trees,
He'll take off your hat without asking you "please,"
He rattles the windows and puffs at a cloud,
Then scoots down the chimney and laughs aloud!

HELEN WING.

## MARJORIE'S ALMANAC

Robins in the treetop,
Blossoms in the grass,
Green things a-growing
Everywhere you pass.
Sudden little breezes,
Showers of silver dew,
Black bow and bent twig,
Budding out anew.

Pine trees and willow trees,
Fringed elm and larch—
Don't you think that Maytime
Is pleasanter than March?

T. B. ALDRICH.

## MAY MORNING

The cherry tree's shedding.
  Its blossoms of May;
Does a fairyland wedding
  Take place to-day?

Bird babies are coming
  And learning to sing,
And the garden's all humming
  With spring!

MARJORIE BARROWS.

## MISTER CARROT

Nice Mister Carrot
Makes curly hair,
His head grows underneath the ground—
His feet up in the air.

And early in the morning
I find him in his bed
And give his feet a great big pull
And OUT comes his head!

DOROTHY ALDIS.

Once there was a snowman
  Stood outside the door
Thought he'd like to come inside
  And run around the floor;

Thought he'd like to warm himself
By the fire light red;
Thought he'd like to climb up
On that big white bed.
So he called the North Wind, "Help me now I pray.
I'm completely frozen, standing here all day."
So the North Wind came along and blew him in the door,
And now there's nothing left of him
But a puddle on the floor.

UNKNOWN.

## PUSSY WILLOWS

I have some dainty pussies here
All dressed in soft gray fur,
But you might listen all day long
And not once hear them purr.

All through the winter's storms and cold,
These furry babies swing,
In cradle beds of shining brown,
On willow branches hung.

But when the days grow long and bright,
And breezes not so cold,
They'll change their dress of silver fur
For robes of green and gold.

MARY E. PLUMMER.

## SPRING WISH

A frog's a very funny thing,
Cool and green in early spring,
Quick and silver through the pool,
With no thought of books or school.

Oh, I want to be a frog,
Running, stretching, on a log,
Blinking there in splendid ease,
Swimming naked when I please,
Nosing into magic nooks,
Quiet marshes, noisy brooks.

Free! And fit for anything!
Oh; to be a frog in spring!

JOHN FARRAR.

Summer is coming! Summer is coming!
How do you think I know?
I found some pussy willows
So I know it must be so.

UNKNOWN.

## SUMMER WISH

I'd like to be a scarecrow,
Swirling in the wheat,
Where I could frighten all the world
And look—oh, far from neat!

The rain would beat upon me,
The wind would brush my hair,
Sweet berries would grow at my feet,
And field mice scuttle there.

I'd see the moon climb up the sky
And there I'd stay and stay,
With no one near to bother me
Or call me in from play!

JOHN FARRAR.

## SWIMMING

When all the days are hot and long
And robin bird has ceased his song,
I go swimming every day
And have the finest kind of play.

I've learned to dive and I can float
As easily as does a boat;
I splash and plunge and laugh and shout
Till Daddy tells me to come out.

It's much too soon; I'd like to cry
For I can see the ducks go by,
And Daddy Duck—how I love him—
He lets his children swim and swim!

I feel that I would be in luck
If I could only be a duck!

CLINTON SCOLLARD.

## THE BEST TIME OF ALL

Green for April, pink for June
  Red and gold for Fall,
But sparkly white for Wintertime,
  The best time of all.

Sing a song of Wintertime—
  Another freezing night,
And all the ruffly, ripply pond
  Was hard and crystal bright.

Then—one to stand and two to start,
  And three—away, away,
With zing! and zoon! Oh, what a tune
  The old pond sings today!

Sing a song of Wintertime,
  Of very trustful birds
Dropping in to call at noon,
  Full of friendly words.

Sing a song of Wintertime,
  A schoolyard full of snow,
Four-and-twenty fleecy tons.
  Sifted high and low.

We made a stoutish gentleman
  Before the morning session,
With buttons down his handsome front
  And such a pleased expression.

He slumped a little when it thawed
  And slimmer seemed to grow;
We liked him—and his pleasant grin
  Was last of all to go.

Snowballs rolling on and on,
  Swelling as they go;
Just how big a ball can get
  Only giants know.

Sing a song of snow and ice;
  Rime a dozen rimes;
Nippy, skippy Wintertime
  Is best of all the times!

NANCY BYRD TURNER.

## THE LEAVES DRINK

Whenever the rain comes gently down,
  It gurgles as it's sinking
Into the ground with sound so low—
  I know the leaves are drinking.

ALICE WILKINS.

## THE MARCH WIND

I come to work as well as play;
I'll tell you what I do;
I whistle all the live-long day,
"Woo-oo-oo-oo! Woo-oo!"

I toss the branches up and down
And shake them to and fro;
I whirl the leaves in flocks of brown,
And send them high and low.

I strew the twigs upon the ground,
The frozen earth I sweep;
I blow the children round and round
And wake the flowers from sleep.

UNKNOWN.

## THE SLEEPY MAPLE TREES

I think they must be sorry—
The little Maple Trees—
That they go to bed too early
To see holidays like these!

They never see Thanksgiving
Nor Hallowe'en at all,
Because they all go fast asleep
So early in the fall.

Poor little tired Maples,
Sleeping in the breeze,
They miss the greatest fun of all—
They can't be Christmas trees!

ELEANOR HAMMOND.

Two little birds one Autumn day,
  Sat on a tree together.
They fluttered about from bough to bough
  Talking about the weather.
"The wind is blowing cold," said they,
  "It chills us as we sing."
So away they flew to the sunny South
  And there they'll stay till spring.

UNKNOWN.

Two little clouds one April day
  Went sailing cross the sky.
They went so fast that they bumped their heads,
  And both began to cry.
The big round sun came out and said,
  "Oh, never mind, my dears,
I'll send all my sunbeams down
  To dry your fallen tears."

UNKNOWN.

## WHICH?

Whenever I'm walking in a wood
I'm never certain whether I should
Shuffle along where the dead leaves fall
Or walk as if I'm not there at all.

It's nice to rustle as hard as you can,
But I can't decide if it's nicer than
Creeping along, while the woodbirds call,
Pretending you are not there at all!

JOYCE L. BRISLEY.

"Who'll rent my house?" a bluebird cried,
  "It's snugly furnished and warm inside,
I am going south for a few winter weeks,
  But the sparrow's my agent, if anyone seeks."

UNKNOWN.

## WINTER

Whenever a snowflake leaves the sky
 It turns and turns to say "Good-bye."
Good-bye, dear clouds, so cool and gray."
 Then turns and hastens on its way.

UNKNOWN.

## WINTER FEATHERS

I looked from my window this morning and found
That Old Mother Snow-Cloud had covered the ground
With feathers and more were still whirling around:
The seeds and the bulbs are her children 'tis said
And so when it's cold from her home overhead
She picks her fat geese and then down on each bed
She drops a soft coverlet, fleecy and white
Which keeps them all warm through the long winter night,
Just as children are tucked in all comfy and tight!

MILDRED D. SHACKLETT.

## WINTER-TIME

Late lies the wintry sun a-bed,
A frosty, fiery sleepy-head;
Blinks but an hour or two; and then,
A blood-red orange, sets again.

Before the stars have left the skies,
At morning in the dark I rise;
And shivering in my nakedness,
By the cold candle, bathe and dress.

Close by the jolly fire I sit
To warm my frozen bones a bit;
Or with a reindeer-sled, explore
The colder countries round the door.

When to go out, my nurse doth wrap
Me in my comforter and cap;
The cold wind burns my face, and blows
Its frosty pepper up my nose.

Black are my steps on silver sod;
Thick blows my frosty breath abroad;
And tree and house, and hill and lake,
Are frosted like a wedding-cake.

ROBERT LOUIS STEVENSON.

## WINTER TREATS

Jack Frost must be a caterer
Like the one who served at Mother's tea—
He's spread refreshments all about
As far as you or I can see.

He's made a lovely frosted cake
From nothing but a pile of leaves,
To the limbs he's hung big lolly pops
And frozen suckers to the eaves!

MILDRED D. SHACKLETT.

## A GOOD PLAY

We built a ship upon the stairs
All made of back bedroom chairs,
And filled it full of sofa pillows
To go a-sailing on the billows.

We took a saw and several nails,
And water in the nursery pails;
And Tom said, "Let us also take
An apple and a slice of cake";—
Which was enough for Tom and me
To go a-sailing on, till tea.

We sailed along for days and days,
And had the very best of plays;
But Tom fell out and hurt his knee,
So there was no one left but me.

ROBERT LOUIS STEVENSON.

## A MODERN DRAGON

A train is a dragon that roars through the dark.
He wriggles his tail as he sends up a spark.
He pierces the night with his one yellow eye,
And all the earth trembles when he rushes by.

ROWENA BASTIN BENNETT.

## A NAUTICAL BALLAD

A capital ship for an ocean trip,
  Was the Walloping Window-blind.
No gale that blew dismayed her crew,
  Nor troubled the captain's mind.

The man at the wheel was taught to feel
  Contempt for the wildest blow;
And it often appeared—when the weather had cleared—
  He had been in his bunk below.

The boatswain's mate was very sedate,
  Yet fond of amusement too;
And he played hopscotch with the starboard watch,
  While the captain tickled the crew.

And the gunner we had was apparently mad,
  For he sat on the after-rail
And fired salutes with the captain's boots
  In the teeth of the booming gale.

The captain sat on the commodore's hat,
  And dined in a royal way,
Off toasted pigs and pickles and figs
  And gunnery bread each day.

The cook was Dutch and behaved as such,
  For the diet he gave the crew,
Was a number of tons of hot cross-buns,
  Served up with sugar and glue.

All nautical pride we laid aside,
  And we cast our vessel ashore,
On the Gulliby Isles, where the Poo-Poo smiles
  And the Rumpletum-Bunders roar.

We sat on the edge of a sandy ledge,
  And shot at the whistling bee:
And the cinnamon bats wore water proof hats,
  As they danced by the sounding sea.

On Rug-gub bark, from dawn till dark,
  We fed, till we all had grown
Uncommonly shrunk; when a Chinese junk
  Came in from the Torrible Zone.

She was stubby and square, but we didn't much care,
  So we cheerily put to sea;
And we left the crew of the junk to chew,
  The bark of the Rug-gub tree.

CHARLES EDWARD CARRYL.

## BOATS

The steamboat is a slow poke,
  You simply cannot rush him.
The sailboat will not move at all
  Without a wind to push him;

But the speed boat, with his sharp red nose,
Is quite a different kind;
He tosses high the spray and leaves
The other boats behind.

ROWENA BASTIN BENNETT.

## CARS GO FAST [1]

Cars go fast along the street,
They're faster than the fastest feet,
And people may ride at their ease
To any little town they please.

Cars go North, South, East, and West,
(I wonder which way is the best!)
On any street they choose to be
Are people walking round like me.

Cars go along on every way
And never tire all the day;
But I should grow quite tired out
If I should always run about.

ANNETTE WYNNE.

## FERRY-BOATS

Over the river,
Over the bay,
Ferry-boats travel
Every day.

Most of the people
Crowd to the side

[1] *Reprinted by permission from "For Days and Days." Copyright, 1919, by Frederick A. Stokes Co.*

Just to enjoy
Their ferry-boat ride.

Watching the seagulls,
Laughing with friends,
I'm always sorry
When the ride ends.

JAMES S. TIPPETT.

## FREIGHT BOATS

Boats that carry sugar
And tobacco from Havana;
Boats that carry cocoanuts
And coffee from Brazil;
Boats that carry cotton
From the city of Savannah;
Boats that carry anything
From any place you will.

Boats like boxes loaded down
With tons of sand and gravel;
Boats with blocks of granite
For a building on the hill;
Boats that measure many thousand
Lonesome miles of travel
As they carry anything
From any place you will.

JAMES S. TIPPETT.

## I SAW A SHIP A-SAILING

I saw a ship a-sailing,
  A-sailing on the sea,
And oh! it was laden
  With pretty things for thee!

There were raisins in the cabin,
  And apples in the hold;
The sails were made of silk,
  And the masts were made of gold.

The four-and-twenty sailors
  That stood between the decks,
Were four-and-twenty white mice,
  With chains about their necks.

The captain was a duck,
  With a jacket on his back;
When the ship began to sail,
  The captain cried, "Quack! quack!"

NURSERY RHYME.

## I'D LIKE TO BE A LIGHTHOUSE

I'd like to be a lighthouse
  All scrubbed and painted white.
I'd like to be a lighthouse
  And stay awake all night
To keep my eye on everything
  That sails my patch of sea;
I'd like to be a lighthouse
  With the ships all watching me.

RACHEL LYMAN FIELD.

## MOTOR CARS

From a city window, 'way up high,
I like to watch the cars go by.
They look like burnished beetles black,
That leave a little muddy track
Behind them as they slowly crawl.
Sometimes they do not move at all

But huddle close with hum and drone
As though they feared to be alone.
They grope their way through fog and night
With the golden feelers of their light.

ROWENA BASTIN BENNETT.

## MY BED IS A BOAT

My bed is like a little boat;
  Nurse helps me in when I embark;
She girds me in my sailor's coat
  And starts me in the dark.

At night, I go on board and say
  Good-night to all my friends on shore;
I shut my eyes and sail away
  And see and hear no more.

And sometimes things to bed I take,
  As prudent sailors have to do;
Perhaps a slice of wedding-cake,
  Perhaps a toy or two.

All night across the dark we steer;
  But when the day returns at last,
Safe in my room, beside the pier,
  I find my vessel fast.

ROBERT LOUIS STEVENSON.

## MY TAXICAB

One day I made a taxicab
Out of a block of wood.
I gave it wheels and steering gear
And the best top that I could.

My taxicab ran down the hall.
It stopped at every door.
It made me piles of money
Which I spread upon the floor.

It carried passengers all day
Till father came at night,
And then I put it safely
In the cupboard out of sight.

JAMES S. TIPPETT.

## PIRATE STORY

Three of us afloat in the meadow by the swing,
Three of us aboard in the basket on the lea.
Winds are in the air, they are blowing in the spring,
And waves are on the meadow like the waves there are at sea.

Where shall we adventure, to-day that we're afloat,
Wary of the weather and steering by a star?
Shall it be to Africa, a-steering of the boat,
To Providence, or Babylon, or off to Malabar?

Hi! but here's a squadron a-rowing on the sea—
Cattle on the meadow a-charging with a roar!
Quick, and we'll escape them, they're as mad as they can be,
The wicket is the harbor and the garden is the shore.

ROBERT LOUIS STEVENSON.

## TAXIS

Ho, for taxis green or blue,
Hi, for taxis red,
They roll along the Avenue
Like spools of colored thread!

*Jack-o'-Lantern yellow,*
*Orange as the moon,*
*Greener than the greenest grass*
*Ever grew in June.*
*Gayly striped or checked in squares,*
*Wheels that twinkle bright,*
*Don't you think that taxis make*
*A very pleasant sight?*
*Taxis shiny in the rain,*
*Scudding through the snow,*
*Taxis flashing back the sun*
*Waiting in a row.*

Ho, for taxis red and green,
  Hi, for taxis blue,
I wouldn't be a private car
  In sober black, would you?

RACHEL LYMAN FIELD.

## THE AIRPLANE

An airplane has gigantic wings
  But not a feather on her breast;
She only mutters when she sings
  And builds a hangar for a nest.
I love to see her stop and start;
She has a little motor heart
That beats and throbs and then is still.
She wears a fan upon her bill.

No eagle flies through sun and rain
So swiftly as an airplane.
I wish she would come swooping down
Between the steeples of the town
And lift me right up off my feet
And take me high above the street,
That all the other boys might see
The little speck that would be me.

ROWENA BASTIN BENNETT.

## THE AIRPLANE [1]

I like to see the airplane and hear the buzzing sound,
And see it settle like a bird quite safely on the ground;
I like to see it spread its wings just like a butterfly,—
You'd think perhaps 'twould find a star to light on in the sky.

ANNETTE WYNNE

## THE FIRST ZEPPELIN

Over the city,
Great ship of grey,
Out of the East you came
One golden day.

Silvered by sunlight,
Nosing along,
Humming contentedly
Your sailing song.

"Someday you'll travel,"
Grandmother said,
"In a long silver ship
High over head."

JAMES S. TIPPETT.

## THE GREEN BUS

Wait a minute,
Green bus!
Slow down!
Stop!

[1] *Reprinted by permission from "For Days and Days." Copyright, 1919, by Frederick A. Stokes Co.*

I will climb
Your winding stair
And ride
On top.

Along
The busy river,
Down
The Avenue,

Any day
I like to take
A trip
With you.

JAMES S. TIPPETT.

## THE KAYAK

Over the briny wave I go,
In spite of the weather, in spite of the snow;
What cares the hardy Eskimo?
In my little skiff, with paddle and lance,
I glide where the foaming billows dance.

Round me the birds slip and soar;
Like me, they love the ocean's roar.
Sometimes a floating iceberg gleams
Above me with its melting streams;
Sometimes a rushing wave will fall
Down on my skiff and cover it all.
But what care I for a wave's attack?
With my paddle I right my little kayak,
And then its weight I speedily trim,
And over the water away I skim.

UNKNOWN.

## THE OLD COACH ROAD

There's hardly a wheel rut left to show
The way the coach road used to go.
Trees straddle it and berries grow
Where coaches rumbled long ago,
And horses' hoofs struck sparks of light,
Many a frosty winter night.
Here gypsy faces, lean and tan,
Peered from some lumbering caravan,
Or peddlers passed with bulging packs
And sheep with sun aslant their backs.
Now, only berry pickers push
Their way through thorn and elder bush—
But sometimes of a night, they say,
Wheels have been heard to pass that way.

RACHEL LYMAN FIELD.

## THE RIVER BRIDGE

Our river is wide; our river is deep;
The bridge across it is long and high.
The twisted cables, the beams and towers
Make a huge drawing upon the sky.

My father and I when we cross the bridge
Have a game which we always play.
The one who sees the most kinds of boats
Is "Captain" or "Skipper" the rest of that day.
My list one day was extremely long
So father made it into a song.

Ferry-boat, steamship,
Freighter, scow,
Tug boat, battleship,
You've got me now.

Cat boat, liner,
Raft, canoe,
Cruiser, yacht,
That's enough for you.

JAMES S. TIPPETT.

## 'SPRESS!

I love to hear the train go by
  With a rumble that tickles my heels.
The choofety-choof of the chimney-stack
  And the clickety-click of the wheels.

WYMOND GARTHWAITE.

## TRAINS

Over the mountains,
Over the plains,
Over the rivers,
Here come the trains.

Carrying passengers,
Carrying mail,
Bringing their precious loads
In without fail.

Thousands of freight cars
All rushing on
Through day and darkness,
Through dusk and dawn.

Over the mountains,
Over the plains,
Over the rivers,
Here come the trains.

JAMES S. TIPPETT.

## TRUCKS

Big trucks for steel beams,
Big trucks for coal,
Rumbling down the broad streets,
Heavily they roll.

Little trucks for groceries,
Little trucks for bread,
Turning into every street,
Rushing on ahead.

Big trucks, little trucks,
In never ending lines,
Rumble on and rush ahead
While I read their signs.

JAMES S. TIPPETT.

## TUGS

Chug! Puff! Chug!
Push, little tug.
Push the great ship here
Close to its pier.

Chug! Puff! Chug!
Pull, strong tug.
Drawing all alone
Three boat-loads of stone.

Busy harbor tugs,
Like round water bugs,
Hurry here and there,
Working everywhere.

JAMES S. TIPPETT.

## WHISTLES [1]

I never even hear
The boats that pass by day;
By night they seem so near,
A-whistling down the bay,
That I can almost understand
The things their whistles say.

I've waked sometimes all warm
In my bed, when eerily
I have heard them out of the dark
A-whistling cheerily
To tell the sleepy folk on land
All's well at sea.

RACHEL LYMAN FIELD.

## UNDERGROUND RUMBLING

At times when we're walking
Along the street
There comes a shivering
Under our feet.

And a hollow, roaring,
Rumbling sound
Seems to come tumbling
Out of the ground.

We've heard it again
And again and again
So of course we know
It's the subway train.

JAMES S. TIPPETT.

[1] *From "Pointed People." By permission of the Macmillan Co.*

## THE ZEPPELIN

The Zeppelin, the Zeppelin!
  He has a fish's tail
And a fish's nose, so I suppose
  He does not need a sail.

The Zeppelin, the Zeppelin!
  He is a flying fish.
The foaming clouds break over him,
  The little breezes swish
Against him like the sea waves.
  Oh, how he loves to swim
Across the sky, and some day I
  Shall take a ride on him.

ROWENA BASTIN BENNETT.

## FOREIGN LANDS

Up into the cherry tree
Who should climb but little me?
I held the trunk with both my hands
And looked abroad on foreign lands.

I saw the next door garden lie,
Adorned with flowers, before my eye,
And many pleasant places more
That I had never seen before.

I saw the dimpling river pass
And be the sky's blue looking-glass;
The dusty roads go up and down
With people tramping into town.

If I could find a higher tree
Farther and farther I should see,
To where the grown-up river slips
Into the sea among the ships.

To where the roads on either hand
Lead onward into fairy land,
Where all the children dine at five,
And all the playthings come alive.

ROBERT LOUIS STEVENSON.

## FROM A RAILWAY CARRIAGE

Faster than fairies, faster than witches,
Bridges and houses, hedges and ditches;
And charging along like troops in a battle,
All through the meadows the horses and cattle:
All of the sights of the hill and the plain
Fly as thick as driving rain;
And ever again, in the wink of an eye,
Painted stations whistle by.

Here is a child who clambers and scrambles,
All by himself and gathering brambles;
Here is a tramp who stands and gazes;
And there is the green for stringing the daisies!
Here is a cart run away in the road
Lumping along with man and load;
And here is a mill and there is a river:
Each a glimpse and gone for ever!

ROBERT LOUIS STEVENSON.

## IN SEPTEMBER

I walked down the lane
  Past the Maple Tree,
And Post Man wind
  Brought a note to me—
A small yellow note
  From my friend the tree!

You call it a "leaf"
  Just drifting down?
Why, it says, "Old Winter
  Will soon be in town!"
So it's really a letter
  The Tree sent down!

ELEANOR HAMMOND.

## MR. COGGS (WATCH-MAKER)

A watch will tell the time of day,
Or tell it nearly, anyway,
Excepting when it's overwound,
Or when you drop it on the ground.

If any of our watches stop,
We haste to Mr. Coggs's shop;
For though to scold us he pretends
He's quite among our special friends.

He fits a dice box in his eye,
And takes a long and thoughtful spy,
And prods the wheels, and says: "Dear, dear!
More carelessness I greatly fear."

And then he lays the dice box down
And frowns a most prodigious frown;
But if we ask him what's the time,
He'll make his gold repeater chime.

EDWARD V. LUCAS.

## THE BALLOON MAN

As you were out a-riding
Did you see the balloon man hiding?
He's hiding to catch the one
Who stole the balloons for fun.

The balloon man doesn't know it,
But the wind took them away.
And as I have told you before,
It was only in play.

MORTON.

## THE CLOCK SHOP

I know a little clock shop
That's very dark and queer
And has—oh, heaps of clocks inside—
A million pretty near.

And there's a funny clock-man
With every sort of key,
Who goes around to all the clocks
And winds 'em up for me.

I listen then, I listen—
And this is what I like—
From little ones to grandfathers
The clocks begin to strike!

And oh! if I am very good,
And coax,—why then,
The clock-man goes to all the clocks
And winds 'em up again!

JEANNETTE C. SHIRK.

## THE COAL MAN

The Coal Man's coming at half-past nine,
The Coal Man's rather a friend of mine.

His face and his hands and his clothes are black,
And coal dust covers each bulging sack.

In every sack is a hundredweight,
And the Coal Man's name is Mr. Tate,

And that's just one of the things I know,
'Cos Kate, the House-maid, told me so.

And though he's old he's terribly strong,
And he's coaling, coaling, all day long.

And Kate says Mr. Tate is white
When he washes his hands and face at night.

But, Mr. Coal Man Tate, you're far,
*Far* nicer, grimy as you are.

HUGH CHESTERMAN.

## THE PEDDLER'S CARAVAN

I wish I lived in a caravan
With a horse to drive, like the peddler-man!
Where he comes from nobody knows,
Or where he goes to, but on he goes!

His caravan has windows two,
And a chimney of tin, that the smoke comes through;
He has a wife, with a baby brown,
And they go riding from town to town.

Chairs to mend, and delf to sell!
He clashes the basins like a bell;
Tea-trays, baskets ranged to order,
Plates, with alphabets round the border!

The roads are brown, and the sea is green,
But his house is like a bathing-machine;
The world is round, and he can ride,
Rumble and slash, to the other side!

With the peddler-man I should like to roam,
And write a book when I came home;
All the people would read my book,
Just like the Travels of Captain Cook!

WILLIAM BRIGHTY RANDS.

## THE POPCORN MAN

Do you hear his whistle blowing—
  Softly blowing as he stands
At the cold and wintry corner,
  With mittens on his hands?

"Popcorn! Popcorn! Five a sack!"
And inside the little wagon,
Through the little steamy window,
You can see the white grains popping
  And hopping round,
Hear a little, crisp, staccato
  Sort of sound,
Watch the fleecy grains go hopping,
  Gaily dancing,
Softly dropping,
Never faltering or stopping,
  Like a fall of fairy snow.

"Popcorn! Popcorn! Five a sack!"
And the children gather round
When they hear the whistle sound,
Staring wide-eyed, wonder-bound,
At the fragrant, snowy mound
  Heaped inside the little window.
They watch his kindly face,
  With his twinkly eyes of black;
They watch his mittened hands
  As he deftly fills each sack.

Oh, I hear his whistle blowing
As through the streets I'm going.
"Popcorn! Popcorn! Five a sack!"
(And I wish I were a child again,
With the years turned back!)

EDITH D. OSBORNE.

## THE POSTMAN[1]

Eight o'clock;
The postman's knock!
Five letters for Papa;
One for Lou,
And none for you,
And three for dear Mamma.

CHRISTINA ROSSETTI.

## THE SHOE-MAKER

As I was a-walking the other day,
I peeped in a window just over the way
And old and bent and feeble too,
There sat an old cobbler a-making a shoe.
With a rack-a-tac-tac and a rack-a-tac-too,
This is the way he makes a shoe.
With a bright little awl he makes a hole,
Right through the upper, and then through the sole.
He puts in a peg, he puts in two,
And a ha-ha-ha-ha and he hammers it thru.

UNKNOWN.

[1] *From "Sing Song." By permission of the Macmillan Co.*

## ACKNOWLEDGMENTS

Thanks are due to the publishers and authors listed below, for permission to use copyrighted selections indicated.

D. Appleton and Company—for "Acorns," "The Beetle," "The Duck," "The Mole," "Pebbles" and "The Rabbit" by Edith King, and "Ring-a-Ring o' Fairies" by M. Nightingale, all from *Fifty New Poems for Children.*

Blackie and Son, London—for "The Apple-Elf" by Sheila Braine, "The Garden Path" by Charlotte Druit Cole and "The Big Arm-Chair" by E. H. R. all from *Blackie's Children's Annual.*

Basil Blackwell—and the authors for "The Happy Sheep" by Wilfred Thorley, "A Tale from the Garden" by Margaret Wynne Jones, "The Spider's Web" by Charlotte Druit Cole, "The Coal Man" by Hugh Chesterman, "The Armadillo" by Lesley Gordon and "My Barrow" by Elizabeth Fleming, all from *The Merry Go Round.*

The Century Company—for "The Little Elf" by John Kendrick Bangs and "The Tides" by Thomas Tapper from *St. Nicholas Magazine,* copyrighted by The Century Company.

The Christian Science Publishing Society and authors—for "Clouds" and "Monday Morning" by Helen Wing, "My Kite" by Beatrice Brown, "Frost" by Ethel Romig Fuller, "Jack-Frost" by Helen Bayley Davis, "Which?" by Joyce L. Brisley and "Taking Turns," "On the Beach," "A Rainy Day," "Autumn Races," "Learning to Skate" and "Welcome Visitors" by Emilie Blackmore Stapp—all from the *Christian Science Monitor.*

The Congregationalist—for "When We Plant a Tree" by Warren P. Landers.

Thos. Y. Crowell—for "Fairy Frilly" and "Christmas Eve" from *The Little White Gate* by Florence Hoatson.

Doubleday, Doran and Company—for "At the Theater," "Vegetables," "The Old Coach Road," "I'd Like to Be a Lighthouse," and "Taxis" from *Taxis and Toadstools* by Rachel Lyman Field—for "Differences," "The Best Game the Fairies Play" and "Very Lovely" from *Fairies and Chimneys,* and "The Fountain" from *Rose Fyleman Fairy Book* by Rose Fyleman.

Evans Brothers, Ltd.—for "The Clock" from *Child Education* by H. S. Bennett.

Good Housekeeping—for "In the Morning" by Cecelia Loftus.

Harper & Brothers—for permission to include extracts from *Bread'n Jam* by Wymond Garthwaite, and *I Go A-Traveling* by James S. Tippett.

Houghton Mifflin Company—The poems by Emma C. Dowd, Abbie Farwell Brown, Frank Dempster Sherman, James R. Lowell, Amy Lowell, T. B. Aldrich, Ralph W. Emerson, Henry W. Longfellow and Mary Carolyn Davies are used by permission of, and arrangement with, Houghton Mifflin Company.

Junior Home Magazine, Inc.—for "Bathtub Bay" by Lenore Riggs, "Popcorn Land" by Elsie F. Kartack, "Lonely Wind" by Eleanor Hammond, "Fairy Aeroplanes" by Anne Blackwell Payne, "Fireflies" and "My Swinging Shadow" by Grace Wilson Coplen, "The Rabbit," "The Hippopotamus" and "The Wolf" by Georgia R. Durston, "Washday" by Elizabeth F. Upson and "Nature's Wash Day" by Marguerite Gode—all from *Junior Home Magazine.*

John Lane, The Bodley Head—for "Jack Frost" from his book *The Child World* by Gabriel Setoun.

Little, Brown & Company—for "A Sleigh-Ride" from *In My Nursery* by Laura E. Richards, "The Grass" from *The Poems of Emily Dickinson,* "The Typewriter" by Mrs. Schuyler Van Rensselaer and "Apple Blossoms" from *Jane, Joseph and John—Their Book* by Ralph Bergengren—all reprinted by permission of Little, Brown & Company.

Lyons and Carnahan—for "Trees Used in Games and Sports" by Mary I. Curtis and "Tree Feelings" by Charlotte Perkins Stetson from *Stories in Trees.*

Ray Long & Richard R. Smith, Inc.—for "Broom," "A Preference," "Summer Wish," "Threnody" and "The Days of the Week" from *Songs for Johnny-Jump-Up* by John Farrar.

Macrae Smith Company—for "Foolish Flowers" by Rupert Sargent Holland.

McLoughlin Bros., Inc.—for "At the Seaside," "The Swing," "The Cow," "Singing," "The Hayloft," "From a Railway Carriage," "Foreign Lands," "My Bed Is a Boat," "A Good Play," "Pirate Story," "Winter Time," "Bed in Summer," "Autumn Fires," "The Sun's Travels," "Foreign Children," "My Shadow," "The

Wind" and "Rain" from *A Child's Garden of Verse* by Robert Louis Stevenson.

Milton Bradley Company—for "Santa Claus and the Mouse" from *In the Child's World* by Emilie Poulsson and "The Valentine's Message" and "When You Send a Valentine" by Mildred J. Hill from *Holiday Songs.*

Minton, Balch & Company—for "Whistles" from *Here, There and Everywhere,* and "Singing," "Brooms," "Ice," "Hot Weather" and "Mister Carrot" from *Everything and Anything*—all by Dorothy Aldis.

Thomas B. Mosher—for "The Lark" and "A Christmas Folk Song" from *A Wayside Flute* by Lizette Woodworth Reese.

New York Times—for "Queen Anne's Lace" by Mary Leslie Newton.

New York Sun—for "Fairy Carpets," "Neighbors," "The Top of Day" and "At Night" by Anne Blackwell Payne.

Outlook Magazine—for "The Gingerbread Man" by Eva Rowland.

F. A. Owen Company—for " 'Tis March" by Hope Nelson, "Meadow Lark," "Chickadee," "Oriole," "Woodpecker," "Crocus," "Lilies of the Valley," "The Sleepy Tulips" and "Quail" by Marion Mitchell Walker, "Guess My Name" by Dora Mon Dore, "The Easter Airplane," by Carolyn R. Freeman, "The Chirrupy Cricket" by Martha B. Thomas and "Raindrops" by Isla P. Richardson—all from *Normal Instructor and Primary Plans.*

Rand McNally & Company—for "Father's Birthday Cake" by Ada Lorraine Jex, "Grandmother's Garden" by Miriam Ott Munson, "A May Basket" by Lilian Bayne West, "Farm Life" by Ruth Edna Stanton and "My Favorite Tree" and "Thanksgiving" by Margaret Munsterberg, from *Child Life.* Rand McNally & Company and the authors for "May Morning" and "The Enchanted Garden" by Marjorie Barrows, "Nobody Knows" by Helen Coale Crew, "An Easter Surprise" by Leona Covey, "At Christmas Time" by Mary Brennan Clapp, "If You've Never" by Elsie M. Fowler, "Rain in April," "Honest Mr. Robin," "A Valentine," "April Fool," "The Sleepy Maple Trees," "March," "St. Patrick's Day" and "In September" by Eleanor Hammond, "The Sea Gull" by Leroy Jackson, "Little Charlie Chipmunk," "Sally Centipede," "Little Danny Donkey" and "Willie Wolf" by Helen Cowles LeCron, "My Airedale Dog" by W. L. Mason, "Hallowe'en" and "Learning to Swim" by Anna Medary, "Whirligig

Beetle" by C. Lindsay McCoy, "Queer Habits" by Corneille McCarn, "The Snow" by Nellie Burget Miller, "The Land Where the Taffy-Birds Grow" by Margaret McBride Hoss, "If I—" by T. C. O'Donnell, "A Little Girl in Bloom" by Anne Blackwell Payne, "Our Circus" by Laura Lee Randall, "The Butterfly" and "Swimming" by Clinton Scollard, "The Clock Shop" by Jeannette C. Shirk, "Kite Tales," "Sing-Time" and "Take Care" by Rose Waldo, "Rainbows," "Tip-Toe Tales," "Smiling" and "She Would" by Dixie Willson, "Turtle-Town," "A Midnight Performance," "Apple Blossoms," "Hallowe'en," "Crickets," "March Wind," "Other Children," "Rain," "A Rock-a-Bye Song" and "Neighbors" by Helen Wing, and "Golden Tacks" by Mildred D. Shacklett—all from *Child Life.*

Thos. Rockwell Company—for "Pussy Willows," "Meeting the Easter Bunny," "The Zeppelin," "The Airplane," "Motor Cars," "Boats," "A Modern Dragon," "Rubber Boots" and "Shell Castles" from *Around a Toadstool Table* by Rowena Bastin Bennett.

George Routledge & Sons—for "The Peddler's Caravan" and "The Wonderful World" from *Posy Ring* by William B. Rands.

Charles Scribner's Sons—for "The Duel" and "Song" by Eugene Field and "The Elf and the Dormouse" and "The Moon" by Oliver Herford.

The Viking Press—for "The Woodpecker," "The Worm," "Water Noises," "The Sky," "The Circus" and "Firefly" from *Under the Tree* by Elizabeth Madox Roberts—copyright, 1922, B. W. Huebsch, Inc.

Ward, Lock & Company—for "There Was a Little Goblin" from *The Wonder Book* by Agnes Grozier Herbertson.

Frederick Warne & Company—for "The Duck and the Kangaroo," "The Quangle Wangle's Hat," "The Owl and the Pussycat," "There Was an Old Man," "The Jumblies" and "There Was a Young Lady" from *Nonsense Book* by Edward Lear.

Wheeler Publishing Company—for "Bedtime" by Helen Coale Crew.

Yale University Press and the authors for "Days" from *Blue Smoke* by Karle Wilson Baker, "Bundles," "Chanticleer," "Catfish," "Alone," "Water-lily," "The Cuckoo Clock," "Roller Skates," "Spring Wish," "The Drum," "Tracks" and "Windmill" from *Songs for Parents* by John Farrar and "The Little Shepherd's Song" from *Enzios Kingdom* by William A. Percy.

Herbert Strang—for "The Dewdrops" by Lydia M. Mackay from *The Violet Book for Children*, "Fairy Umbrellas" by Lucy Diamond and "Pipes and Drums" by Lilian Holmes from *Mrs. Strang's Annual for Children,* published by Oxford University Press.

To the following authors:

Mr. A. P. Bridgman for "A Top," "A Chair," "Bow and Arrow," "A Saw," "Buttons," "Toes," "A Wave," "Dandelions," "A Key," "Peanuts," "Pop Corn," "A Fish," "Book" and "Pussy Willow" from *Guess*—Dodge Publishing Company by L. J. Bridgman.

Emily Rose Burt for "The Popcorn Party" and "For April Showers" from *Woman's Home Companion* and "The Escape" from *St. Nicholas Magazine.*

Grace Glaubitz for "Walking" from *Junior Home Magazine.*

Mr. Hausgen for "A Lovely Bed," "Her Choice" and "The Spider Web" from *Child Life* by Mattie Lee Hausgen.

Leroy Jackson for "Hippity Hop to Bed" from *Woman's Home Companion.*

Arthur A. Knipe for "A Discovery," "Autumn" and "Thirsty Flowers" from *Remember Rhymes* by Penn Publishing Company.

C. Lindsay McCoy for "Hornets," "Snail," "Devil's Darning Needle," "Honey Bee," "Katy-Did," "Lady Bug" and "Caroline Cricket."

Nellie Burget Miller for "Our House," "The Mist," "Little Day Moon" and "Morning Clouds."

Christopher Morley for "Dandy Dandelion," "Smells" and "Animal Crackers."

Anne Blackwell Payne for "Robin" from *New York Evening Post* and "Ambition" from *To-day's Housewife* and "Silver Sheep."

Ethel Robb for "Child's Evensong" and "Christmas 'Good Night.' "

Mildred D. Shacklett for "A Sometimes Wish," "Autumn Gloves," "Autumn Train," "Belonging to Summer," "Broadcasting," "Deep in the Woods," "Four Kinds of Wading," "Movies in the Fire," "Mud-cakes (A Good Recipe)," "The Swing Ship," "Winter Feathers" and "Winter Treats."

Nancy Byrd Turner for "A Pop Corn Song" from *St. Nicholas Magazine* and "The Best Time of All" from *Ladies' Home Journal.*

Gertrude Van Winkle for "My Radio," "Static," "Magic Waves" and "The Microphone."

Helen Hay Whitney for "The Cat" from *Verses for Jack and Joan.*

Alice Wilkins for "A Little Frog," "Fun on the Beach," "Little Brown Bear," "The Elephant's Trunk," "Ways of Traveling," "The Ducks," "Fairies' Lights," "New Shoes," "My Funny Umbrella," "Snow" and "The Leaves' Drink."

In some cases where poems or verses are not acknowledged, the compilers have searched diligently to find sources—to get permission to use them—but without success. Other poems are not included, because they are not available for anthologies.

# INDEX TO AUTHORS

# INDEX TO FIRST LINES

# INDEX TO INTEREST

## *ACTIVITIES AND PLAYTHINGS*

### *Boat*



### *Climbing*



### *Digging*



### *Doll*



### *Fishing*

*Kites*



*Miscellaneous*



*Out-of-Doors*

*Pets*



*Store*



*ANIMALS*

*Cat*



*Chipmunk* and *Squirrel*



*Circus*

*Cow*



*Dog*



*Elephant*



*Fish*



*Frog*



*Horse*



*Kitten.* See *Cat*

*Miscellaneous*

### *Turtle*



### *Worm*



## *BIRDS*

### *Bluebird*



### *Chickadee*



### *Chickens* and *Ducks*



### *Lark*



### *Miscellaneous*

*Owl*



*Robin*



*Thrush*



*Woodpecker*

## *FAIRIES*



## *FARM*

## *FLOWERS*

### *Apple Blossoms*



### *Crocus*



### *Daisies*



### *Dandelions*



### *Miscellaneous*

*Pussy Willow*



*HISTORICAL*

## *HOLIDAYS*

### *Arbor Day*



### *Christmas*



### *Easter*



### *Hallowe'en*



### *Miscellaneous*

*Thanksgiving*



*Valentine Day*



*HOME*

### *INSECTS*

*Bee*



*Beetle*



*Butterfly* and *Caterpillar*

## *JUST FOR FUN*



## *LULLABIES*

*MISCELLANEOUS*



*NATURAL PHENOMENA*

*Brook*



*Clouds*

*Hills*



*Jack Frost*



*Leaves*



*Miscellaneous*

### *Moon*



### *Rain*

*Rainbow*



*Sea*



*Sea Shells*



*Sky*

*Snow*



*Stars*



*Sun*



*Trees*

*RELIGIOUS*



*RIDDLES*

## *SEASONS*

### *Autumn*

*Spring*

*Summer*



*Winter*

## *TRANSPORTATION*

### *Aircraft*



### *Boats*



### *Miscellaneous*

*Train*



*TRAVEL*



*WORKMEN AND SHOPS*